NATURE
STRIKES
BACK

The sea can be an awesome foe. Swells 35 feet high, winds of 50 knots, and snow squalls can batter ships so that they simply roll over and die. Crewmen in this photo are huddled in the bow of the British motor ship Ambassador. The rescue operations of the U. S. Coast Guard cutter Coos Bay are being hampered by wild seas. The 25-foot seas are heaving spume in 40-knot winds.

NATURE
STRIKES
BACK

John Gabriel Navarra

PUBLISHED FOR THE AMERICAN MUSEUM OF NATURAL HISTORY
THE NATURAL HISTORY PRESS   GARDEN CITY, NEW YORK
1971

The Natural History Press, publisher for The American Museum of Natural History, is a division of Doubleday & Company, Inc. Directed by a joint editorial board made up of members of the staff of both the Museum and Doubleday, The Natural History Press publishes books in all branches of the life and earth sciences, including anthropology and astronomy. The Natural History Press has its editorial offices at Doubleday & Company, Inc., 277 Park Avenue, New York, New York 10017, and its business offices at 501 Franklin Avenue, Garden City, New York 11530.

Church destroyed by Hurricane Camille.

Preface

Each year natural disasters claim thousands of lives in every corner of the earth. No nation is immune. Earthquakes, tornadoes, floods, droughts, tropical storms, lightning, fire, avalanches, landslides, and blizzards strike and produce a harvest of death.

The death toll for any single year can be impressive. The year 1962 produced what might be considered a normal record: An earthquake in Iran on September 1 claimed more than twenty thousand lives. Earlier—in January of the same year—a landslide in Peru caused four thousand deaths. And these two disasters were by no means the only ones that occurred in 1962.

In the span of only a few years, natural disasters disrupt hundreds of thousands of lives. A pair of tsunamis, for example, in 1960, smashed into the east coast of Pakistan and killed more than ten thousand people. A year earlier, in 1959, a hurricane

claimed fifteen hundred lives in Mexico. During the same year, forty-five hundred people were lost in Japan when a typhoon struck. The world-wide toll for 1959 was more than ten thousand lives sacrificed in various kinds of storms.

As we look back over the years, it is appalling to read about the devastation caused by natural disasters. Western Europe is no stranger to calamity, but it is shocking, nevertheless, to learn that a tide in 1953 left two thousand dead. India seems to be a land of monumental tragedy. In 1942, for example, a hurricane struck and killed eleven thousand. And then, before the people could recover, a tsunami engulfed the coast and claimed another ten thousand lives. China, with its enormous population, appears to have been singled out for special punishment. Floods in 1887 took 900,000 lives. Then, in 1911, another hundred thousand Chinese fell before rampaging flood waters.

These events of the past may seem remote. But it is just as appalling to contemplate the awesome destruction that future natural disasters may create. The decade of the seventies, for example, started with a devastating earthquake in Turkey that came on the heels of typhoons in the Pacific and avalanches in Switzerland and France. Spring 1970 in the Northern Hemisphere brought tornadoes to Texas and the Midwest, while Rumania experienced its worst floods since Roman times. On Sunday, May 31, 1970, Peru was devastated by an earthquake that claimed more than thirty thousand lives. The heat of the summer that followed helped spawn hurricanes in the Gulf of Mexico. In fact, the hurricane season of 1970 started early in the spring. On May 20, 1970, a tropical storm developed hurricane-force winds of eighty miles per hour and thus became known as Hurricane Alma. This was only the second tropical storm in this century to reach hurricane-force winds in May.

Although some countries seem to be struck more than others, no nation in the world is a safe haven beyond the reach of nature's grasp. Italy, a tourist's paradise, has been shaken by frequent earthquakes, violent eruptions, and storms that devastate the landscape, claim lives, and destroy art treasures. Recall the floods that inundated Florence during the 1960s, and the pitiful plight of Venice which is even today slowly sinking into the sea. The United States has suffered its losses over the years, too. The Alaskan earthquake of 1964 is only one example.

We are fond of referring to Mother Earth. We tend to picture man being cuddled to the bosom of a hospitable, warm, generous planet. But when you think of the forces of nature that reach out to engulf man, you begin to visualize him hanging precariously to an earth that is anything but motherly. The environment is, in fact, quite hostile.

The death toll that results from natural disasters occurs despite our competency in science and technology. There is very little possibility that we can control these forces of nature. What we can do is learn to predict when they will be unleashed. Then we must also learn how to warn people and how to help them to protect themselves. Disasters occur because nature strikes when we are unprepared.

We must somehow harness our understanding of science and our capabilities in technology for keeping the country alert to the forces of nature that surround and strike at us. If we use our science and technology well, we can develop prediction and warning systems that will save lives and help man adjust to the awesome natural forces of the environment that are a perennial threat to his survival.

John Gabriel Navarra

Farmingdale, New Jersey

Hurricane Debbie, with its large eye clearly visible, is seen in the center of the picture. The storm was photographed by satellite, ESSA 9, as it swept across the sea 500 miles northeast of Puerto Rico.

CONTENTS

Army Corps of Engineers, pp. 132, 137.

Cinerama Releasing Corporation, p. 203.

Consulate General of Iceland, p. 205.

Consulate General of Japan, pp. 51, 150.

ESSA, pp. 8, 18, 57, 58, 60, 81, 82, 83, 92, 103, 112, 116, 117(top), 123, 128, 187, 211.

French Cultural Services, pp. 157, 159, 161, 162.

NASA, p. 14.

National Park Service, p. 39.

Celeste Navarra, pp. 20–21, 36, 41, 44, 47, 48, 54, 95, 96, 97, 136, 139, 144, 182, 190, 209.

Skip Nelson, KSTP Films, p. 147.

Swiss National Tourist Office, pp. 142, 193.

University of Miami Radar Lab, p. 78.

U. S. Air Force, pp. 76, 126.

U. S. Coast Guard, pp. 2, 5, 64, 117(bottom), 195, 200.

U. S. Department of Agriculture, pp. 166, 169, 170, 179.

U. S. Forest Service, pp. 72, 75, 88, 89.

U. S. Geological Survey, pp. 28, 30.

U. S. Navy, p. 105.

NATURE
STRIKES
BACK

1. Earthquakes

Astronaut L. Gordon Cooper took this photo from the command pilot's window of the Gemini 5 spacecraft. Spread before us is a view of Mexico and Baja California, looking southeast.

1. *Earthquakes*

The Gulf of California is really a crack, or tear, in the earth's surface that goes more than thirty miles deep. It was formed slowly over the ages by the drift of Baja California and southern California away from the Mexican mainland. This movement is continuing. It is going on today—at this very moment!

Baja California is not unique. In many areas of our earth, masses of land hundreds of miles long are slowly moving along great tears or faults in the surface. The land along the San Andreas Fault in California is only one example of a traveling mass. It moves approximately one foot during a six-year period.

The greatest number of tears and moving chunks of land occur along the border of the Pacific Ocean. There are major faults in the earth's surface in New Zealand, the Philippines, Taiwan, and Chile. Slow horizontal movement is the most prevalent type of motion along these faults. Such movement is, of course, less spectacular than a sudden vertical movement. But movement of any kind can, and often does, culminate in a rumbling earthquake.

The descriptions of earthquakes in story and more recently in the popular press have painted into history frightful pictures of fleeing refugees, widespread destruction, and complete chaos. And so it is not unusual for the word "earthquake" itself to stir our imaginations with scenes of devastation and concern for the people in the disaster area.

Most natural hazards—a hurricane, for example—can be detected, followed, and studied. If we are alert, ample warning can be given as the threat develops and matures. In a sense, we can do something to prepare for an impending disaster that we can see coming. An earthquake, on the other hand, is a special kind of natural disaster. It seems to come without warning because we have not been very successful in learning how to detect the conditions that produce it.

When you visit the scene of an earthquake or see photographs of ruined schools, stores, houses, and industrial plants, you get the feeling that a giant has seized the buildings and twisted them. To an uninformed observer, there is almost no other way to describe the destruction. The land truly looks as though it has been struck and torn by titanic fingers. It is not surprising that ancient people felt that an earthquake represented the vengeance of the gods.

In almost every earthquake disaster recorded, there is a simple, consistent story: One day the life of a city is going on normally and peacefully; then, without warning, the violent rumbling comes. The houses and public buildings are thrown hither and yon. Tumbled heaps of stone, brick, timber, and steel litter the disrupted pattern of the city. And, in most cases, the bodies of thousands of people lie buried in the ruins.

The twentieth century has produced some spectacular stories of destruction. An earthquake in Kansu, China, in 1920, for example, claimed the lives of over 100,000 people. Three years later, more than 142,000 people were lost in a Japanese earthquake. The United States has had its share of problems, too. In 1906, San Francisco suffered its most famous earthquake. The movement, rumbling, and the fire that followed killed nearly seven hundred and left the city in ruins. San Francisco was, of course, rebuilt, and today homes surround the San Andreas Fault.

After the San Francisco earthquake, the quake problems in the United States moved south, and in 1925 the city of Santa Barbara experienced a heavy shock that wrecked many buildings. Then eight years later, on March 10, 1933, a violent earthquake wrecked parts of Long Beach, California, and other towns near Los Angeles.

Thirty-one years after the Long Beach quake, the action was in the north again. To many of us, the Alaskan earthquake of March 27, 1964, was a natural disaster for which we were completely unprepared. The movement and shock released twice as much energy as the San Francisco earthquake of 1906. It ripped through south central Alaska and was felt over an area of almost 500,000 square miles.

The ground motion of the Alaskan earthquake at the center of destruction was so violent that the tops of some trees were snapped off. An official count numbered more than one hundred dead. The loss of life and property, however, would have been far greater had Alaska been more densely populated. Even so, the property damage was placed at more than $500 million. On top of this, a second earthquake rocked an isolated section of southwestern Alaska just two days later.

The Peruvian earthquake of Sunday, May 31, 1970, was a dismal picture of thousands of buildings destroyed, a number of cities demolished, and entire villages "erased from the map." More than 200,000 persons were left homeless. The death toll reached at least thirty thousand because the quake ripped away natural dikes on lakes high in the Andes Mountains.

We see the damage (along 4th Avenue, Anchorage, Alaska) produced by the Prince William Sound earthquake. The epicenter was about ninety miles from this point.

In this photo, we are viewing the details of the ground slumping that took place immediately under the Denali sign. The first floor is completely below the sidewalk level.

Certain areas of the earth seem to be plagued more than others by earthquakes. Scientists studying the problem have confirmed this observation as a fact and developed seismic risk maps that divide the earth into four zones. Zone 0, according to the seismic risk map, is a location where there is no reasonable expectation of earthquake damage. In areas designated as Zone 1, minor damage can occur. Zone 2 locations are those in which moderate damage can be expected. A Zone 3 area, according to this scheme of classification, is a high-risk zone and one in which major destructive earthquakes may occur.

Southern Florida—the Miami and Key West area—is classified as Zone 0. In the western panhandle section of Florida, the southern portion of Alabama, and the extreme southeastern tip of Mississippi around Mobile, there is no reasonable expectation of earthquake damage. The central and southern sections of Texas around Corpus Christi are given a Zone 0 classification, too.

New Jersey, Maryland, Delaware, and New York City are Zone 1 areas. North Dakota, South Dakota, Minnesota, Wisconsin, Iowa, Colorado, and Michigan are classified as minor damage zones. Eastern North Carolina is also a Zone 1 area, but western North Carolina is given a Zone 2 classification.

The area around Charleston, South Carolina, is clearly a Zone 3 area. A destructive earthquake, in fact, occurred in Charleston in 1886. Another high-risk zone exists where Illinois, Kentucky, Tennessee, Arkansas, and Missouri have common borders. Charleston, Missouri, located in this area, experienced a destructive earthquake in 1895.

A rather large Zone 3 area runs from the Manhattan section of Montana, south to Hebgen Lake taking in the extreme northwestern section of Wyoming, the eastern section of Idaho, including Pocatello, as well as the western section of Utah. Western Nevada is also considered a high-risk location. The Zone 3 area that includes western Nevada extends into California running from the Imperial Valley north through Los Angeles

The San Andreas Lake is located in the canyon and deep gullies of the San Andreas Fault zone alongside State Highway 35 on the San Francisco

on to Santa Barbara and San Francisco, and then spreads northward beyond San Francisco. The Puget Sound area of the state of Washington is classified as a high-risk area, too.

When you consider the world situation, it is apparent that a great majority of earthquakes occur in areas bordering the Pacific Ocean. Taken collectively, these high-risk zones are referred to as a circumpacific belt, or "ring of fire." The belt includes the Pacific coasts of North and South America, the Aleutians, Japan, Southeast Asia, and Australia.

peninsula. This lake serves as a reservoir for the city. What will happen to the water if there is movement along the San Andreas Fault?

A second belt of great activity is along the mid-Atlantic ridge. A fish skeleton figure of transverse cracks runs through this underwater ridge. These cracks, or fissures, are results of earthquake activity.

A third major earthquake belt branches from the "ring of fire" in the Pacific and arcs across southeastern and southern Asia into southern Europe. This high-risk zone extends through the Indian Ocean and into the eastern Mediterranean. Iran, located along this belt, was struck by an earthquake in 1968 that claimed eleven thousand lives. Lisbon is at the western end of this same belt. In 1755, an earthquake that occurred in this capital city of Portugal claimed more than sixty thousand lives.

In any normal year, several million tremors originate along these three world-wide belts. The earthquakes range from barely detectable wiggles to great movements which disrupt anything and everything on the earth's surface. The Alaskan quake of 1964, for example, caused one-third of Alaska to tilt.

Millions of people in the United States live in potential earthquake areas. Schools, high-rise apartments, and other housing developments have been built in many locations where the danger of major destructive earthquakes is very real. Some great dams are used to store trillions of gallons of water in these same high-risk areas. Imagine the kind of destruction that might result if a dam happened to be split open by a quake.

Nuclear reactors are a necessary part of progress, but too many proposals have been made to construct them in locations where there is high earthquake risk. Only after a six-year pitched battle did the Pacific Gas and Electric Company, for example, announce on October 30, 1964 that it had abandoned plans for a nuclear generating plant at Bodega Bay, California. The site was only 1,000 feet west of the San Andreas Fault. As more of these installations are needed to generate electric power, there is a real danger that some will be placed in high-risk areas. Power plants, remember, require enormous quantities of cooling water. And in arid California the most desirable sites for nuclear plants are along the coast. But the San Andreas fault zone runs nearly the whole length of this coast. If a nuclear installation is ruptured during an earthquake, consider how this will compound the tragedy.

There is a very urgent need for information concerning the nature, causes, and effects of earthquakes. We have some information; but it is far from adequate, and it does not give us the grasp of the situation that is needed for today's world. Consider for a moment that we inhabit less than one-quarter of the earth's surface and we have explored much less than a thousandth of its 8,000-mile diameter. Below our cities, villages, farms, roads, railroad tracks, and mines lie the unvisited depths of the earth. And remember, it is from these hidden regions that tremendous forces cause huge dislocations in the earth's crust.

With respect to the earth, it is very difficult to develop a proper concept of size relationships. Man himself is small, puny, and insignificant alongside a mountain. Therefore, mountains tend to loom large in our perspective of the earth. For most of us, the Himalayas seem to reach upward and scrape the heavens. Relative sizes and dimensions usually elude our grasp unless we can refer to a model that is within our experience. In some ways, a peach is a good model of our earth because it can be used for comparisons to establish size relationships.

The earth has a skin just as a peach does. The earth's skin, of course, was formed as its outer molten material cooled and froze. We refer to this frozen section of the earth as a crust. A peach skin is about $\frac{1}{200}$ as thick as the peach. The earth has a diameter of about 8,000 miles. The earth's crust would need to be forty miles thick to be $\frac{1}{200}$ of the diameter of the earth. In other words, if the crust were forty miles thick, it would be relatively as thick as the peach skin. The crust of the earth is, in fact, as much as twenty-five miles thick over continental areas under the mountain systems, and as thin as two or three miles under the oceans. The crust, at its thickest spots, is only $\frac{1}{400}$ of the earth's diameter. We are thus talking about an earth skin that is relatively only half as thick as a peach skin.

Let's continue the analogy: The skin of a peach is held up by its pulp. The pulp of the peach extends about halfway to its center. In the case of the earth, the pulp is an area called the *mantle*. It is about 2,000 miles thick and consists of non-metallic mineral matter sometimes called *magma*. The earth started out as a searing, hot mass of material. Thus, the magma that holds up the crust or outer layer of rocks all over the world is quite hot. Note that the magma extends about halfway to the center of the earth, just as the pulp of a peach does. At the base of the earth's mantle, the pressure is about 11,000 tons per square inch. The temperatures within the mantle range around 2,500° F. The magma, or mantle material, behaves like a very sluggish fluid at these tremendous temperatures and pressures.

The center of a peach is filled by a hard pit. The earth's center is called the *core*. Its "pit" is a hot mass of iron containing a small amount of nickel. Temperatures within the iron-nickel core are greater than 4,000° F. The hot core consists of two sections: an inner and an outer core. The earth's inner core is a solid ball surrounded by the fluid outer core. The density of the core is nearly 600 pounds per cubic foot. High pressures make the core more dense than iron found near the surface. The average density of surface iron is only 450 pounds per cubic foot.

Now let's push our analogy one step further: If a peach is allowed to dry in the sun, the inside shrivels and becomes smaller. As the pulp shrinks, the peach skin puckers into ridges and creases. Scientists believe that the "pulp" of the earth has cooled slowly over the billions of years since its creation. This slow cooling has caused the interior of the earth to shrink ever so slightly. As a result, the outer skin or surface layer of rocks has puckered into ridges and creases over the shrinking interior.

Strip off a piece of paper-thin peach skin. Look at it and compare it to the diameter of the peach. Remember that the peach skin has about the same relationship to the peach as the crust, or surface layer of rocks, has to the diameter of the earth. In other words, the highest mountains as well as the deepest ocean trenches are all contained in the paper-thin creases that make up the earth's crust. The Himalayas are really no greater blemishes on the earth's surface than the wrinkles in the skin of a peach.

This picture of the true relative thickness of the earth's crust and creases is important. The destructive effects of an earthquake, after all, are felt when the comparatively thin "peach skin" of the earth is disrupted and made to move. The forces which produce the earthquake, however, may be generated and developed in a zone that ranges from the crust to a depth of more than 450 miles.

The continents—North and South America, Europe, Australia, Africa, Asia, and Antarctica—are the portions of the earth's crust that happen to be above sea level. The bottoms of the oceans surrounding the continents are also made up of the frozen crust of the earth and ride on the hot, molten magma. The ocean basins represent extensive depressions in the "peach-skin" crust of the earth.

There is a temperature difference between the white-hot region of the inner core and the relatively cooler region of the mantle near the crust. This difference drives slow-moving cycles of rising and descending currents in the mantle material below the crust. Some scientists suggest that these currents rise beneath the thin-crusted ocean floor and create a constant upward thrust on the mid-ocean ridges. The stress of this upward thrust produces spinelike, transverse cracks in the ocean floor. The magma that wells up and forces its way through replaces and spreads the old sea floor. As a result of this movement, shallow earthquakes are produced in the thin crust of the ocean floor.

The upwelling and push generated by the magma as it spreads the sea floor also causes the currents to begin their descent at the edges of the continents. The descending currents produce compressive pressures in the crust of the continental areas. In turn, the compression causes massive folding which leads to the formation of trenches and the uplift of mountain ranges. The regions in which these events occur are the sites of the deeper earthquakes.

The convection currents cause a great deal of stress and strain in the crust and upper mantle. The rock structures of the crust are actually deformed. If the pent-up energy is released slowly, the rock yields and gradually takes on a new shape. On the other hand, when the stress builds too rapidly, large blocks of the earth's crust are bent and strained to the breaking point. If the stress causes the rocks to rupture, the huge blocks rebound and move violently. Destructive quakes are caused by this dislocation of the earth's crust.

In the case of a violent dislocation, the energy is released in one large wrench followed by smaller tremors. The tremors are referred to as "*aftershocks.*" The aftershocks are produced by continuing collapse and movement of crustal blocks along the line of the fracture. Sometimes the violent wrench or shift of the earth's crust is preceded by small structural failures which produce foreshocks. The foreshocks are really small tremors.

In any event, the energy that accumulates as a result of rising and descending convection currents in the earth's mantle must be dissipated. In most cases, it is released in the form of heat, sound, and mechanical movement. The combination of effects is called an *earthquake.* An earthquake, therefore, is nothing more than the oscillatory and sometimes violent movement of the earth's surface that follows a release of energy.

There are two general types of vibrations produced by earthquakes: *surface waves* and *body waves.* These earthquake, or seismic, waves are generated as the crust breaks and snaps to a new position. The seismic waves are the shakers and wreckers that accompany the release of energy.

Surface waves are so named because they travel along the earth's surface. They produce most of the destruction because they actually make the ground roll. Surface waves are usually stronger than body waves.

The seismic vibrations called body waves are sometimes referred to as preliminary waves since they arrive before the surface or rolling waves. There are, however, two different and distinct types of body waves. The first is classified as a *compression wave,* while the second type is said to be a *sheer wave.*

The compression waves travel at great speeds. They ordinarily are the first signals that indicate an earthquake has occurred and are referred to as the primary, or P, waves. A P wave arrives at the surface like a hammer blow. The blow is the result of energy released deep within the earth. P waves—like sound waves—move through both liquids and solids by compressing the material directly ahead of them. Each compressed particle, in turn, springs back to its original position as the energy moves on. The blow of a P wave travels in the same way that a bump from a locomotive on one freight car travels clear through a long train.

The P wave is the swiftest seismic wave. Its speed, however, varies with the material through which it passes. P-wave velocity in the crust of the earth usually is less than four miles per second, or 15,000 miles per hour. But just below the crust of the earth, the speed of a P wave jumps to five miles per second. As a P wave passes deep into the earth and moves through the core, its speed increases to eight and one-half miles per second. Thus, it travels through the core of the earth at more than 30,000 miles per hour. When a P wave strikes an object embedded in the ground, it produces a series of sharp pushes and pulls. These pushes and pulls are in a direction parallel to the wave path.

The second type of body wave, on the other hand, produces a sheering effect or a side-to-side shaking of an object embedded in the ground. These sheer waves are referred to as secondary, or S, waves. One reason for the sheer waves to be called secondary is that they ordinarily reach the surface after the P wave. The sheer, or S, waves displace an object at right angles to their direction of travel and are thus sometimes called *transverse* waves. The S wave must have a rigid medium through which to move. These transverse or sheer waves are not found to travel below the mantle. This fact tends to support the theory that the outer core is, in fact, liquid.

27

An earthquake struck Varto, Turkey, in June, 1967.

Let's stop for a moment and put all of this information together. The first signal you get that an earthquake has occurred will often be a sharp thud. The thud, or hammer blow, indicates the arrival of the compression, or P, waves. Then the P waves are followed by the sheer, or S, waves. With the arrival of S waves, objects begin to shake from side to side. And then when the surface waves arrive, the ground begins to roll.

The vibrations produced by earthquakes can be recorded and measured by an instrument called a *seismograph*. The principle of the seismograph is rather simple: Place a half dollar on a scratch pad which you are holding horizontally in your hand. Move the pad suddenly forward and then back. Now, just as suddenly, move the pad sideways and then back. The half dollar tries to remain in one place while the scratch pad slips about under it. A seismograph is nothing more than an instrument which has a heavy weight supported clear of the ground and freely suspended.

When P, S, and surface waves travel through the earth to a seismograph, they shake the supports on which the weight hangs. But the weight, because of its inertia, tends to remain steady in one place. A recording needle, or pen, attached to the weight is used to trace a graph on a revolving drum which is attached to the supports of the apparatus. In other words, body waves (P and S) and the surface waves shake the supports of the seismograph. In turn, the supports shake the revolving drum and the paper on it. Everything shakes except the steady mass of the weight and the pen attached to it. In this way, a pen writes a record of the vibrations.

The zigzag line made by the pen of a seismograph is called a *seismogram*. The data recorded in a seismogram allow the scientist to describe the earthquake. The recorded amplitude of the P, S, and surface waves, for example, indicates the amount of energy released. By combining data from selected seismograph stations, the epicenter and the focal depth of an earthquake can also be located.

The focal depth of an earthquake is the depth below the surface at which the energy originates, the *focus*. Scientists refer to earthquakes as being either shallow, intermediate, or deep. The focus of a shallow earthquake is less than 38 miles from the surface of the earth. An earthquake with a focal depth from 38 to 188 miles is classified as intermediate. A deep earthquake has its focus below 188 miles.

The deepest earthquake recorded has not had its focus below 450 miles. This means that most earthquakes are concentrated in the crust and upper mantle. Earthquakes, for example, which occur in California along the San Andreas Fault have had rather shallow focal depths. The focus or location at which the energy originates has, for most of them, been less than 10 miles below the surface.

The point on the earth's surface directly above the focus is referred to as the *epicenter*. The location of an earthquake is commonly reported by giving the geographic position of its

The damage caused by an earthquake in Caracas was rather extensive in 1967.

epicenter. The time and arrival of the compression and sheer waves at selected seismograph stations is used to locate the epicenter of an earthquake.

Two scales are used to describe the severity of an earthquake: the Richter scale and the modified Mercalli scale. The Richter scale measures an earthquake in terms of its energy. The magnitude as expressed by the Richter scale is a measure of the amplitude of the seismic waves based on instrument records. The second scale, the Mercalli scale, is based on personal observations. In other words, the Mercalli scale attempts to describe the actual effect or intensity of an earthquake at a particular location. The Richter and Mercalli scales are completely separate in intent. They should not be confused. The Mercalli scale is a subjective measure at a particular location. It attempts to describe the damage to life and property.

Actually, the Richter magnitude scale gives a measure of the energy released by an earthquake at its point of origin. In order to assign a number on the Richter scale, the measurement must be based on a seismogram made at a distance of sixty-two miles from the epicenter. Most stations that record earthquakes, however, are bound to be at some distance other than sixty-two miles. This means that seismograms from several different stations are studied. Then complex conversion tables are used to arrive at the final or standard figure.

The Richter scale actually has no fixed maximum. It does not rate the size of an earthquake on a scale of 10. A magnitude 5 earthquake, for example, releases energy equivalent to that which would be released by one thousand tons of TNT. A magnitude of 7 on the Richter scale indicated that the energy released is equivalent to about one million tons of TNT. An earthquake of magnitude 2 is the smallest that would normally be felt or sensed by a human observer. Any earthquake with a Richter value of 6 or more is commonly considered to be a major disturbance. The Alaskan earthquake of March 27, 1964, was described as having a magnitude of about 8.5 on the Richter scale.

The modified Mercalli intensity scale grades the earthquake by describing the kinds of damage and effects caused by it. According to the Mercalli scale, an earthquake may vary in intensity from Degree I to Degree XII. A Degree I earthquake, for example, is not felt except by a few people under especially favorable conditions. A Degree II earthquake on the Mercalli intensity scale is felt by people, and it causes delicately suspended objects to swing. A Degree IV earthquake cracks walls and produces the sensation that a heavy truck has just struck a building. A Degree IX rating on the Mercalli scale is given to an earthquake which shifts buildings off foundations and conspicuously cracks them. An earthquake which leaves few, if any, masonry structures standing, destroys bridges, and produces broad fissures in the ground is given a rating of XI on the Mercalli scale. An earthquake with a rating of XII is one in which the damage is total and waves are seen on ground surfaces. The Alaskan quake of 1964 was rated as X on the Mercalli scale. Landslides, rockfalls, and slumps in river banks were part of the destruction caused by the Alaskan quake. The San Francisco quake of 1906 had a rating of XI.

Now, it should be clear that there is a difference between the Richter and the Mercalli scale. An earthquake of large magnitude, as measured by the Richter scale, may not necessarily cause intense surface effects. In such a circumstance, the earthquake would be given a very low rating on the Mercalli scale. The effect as measured by the Mercalli scale in a given region depends to a large extent on local surface and subsurface conditions. An area, for example, underlain by unstable ground such as sand, clay, or some other unconsolidated sediments is likely to experience more noticeable surface effects than an area that is equally distant from the epicenter but underlain instead by granite or firm ground.

The importance of the condition of the underlying ground was forcefully demonstrated in the Alaskan earthquake of 1964. The town of Whittier was built on firm granite. It suffered very little damage from the seismic waves although it was close to the epicenter. In Anchorage, which was much farther from the epicenter, there was much greater destruction of the homes and buildings constructed on unstable slopes underlain by clay.

At the present time, our capability to predict the time, place, and size of earthquakes is very limited. Slight progress has been made in predicting that an earthquake of a given magnitude may occur within a region. But such predictions do not pinpoint the time, place, and size with any precise degree of accuracy. There is a clear need for long-range studies that sharpen our ability to predict earthquakes. The best that can be said, at the present time, is that you should avoid building certain types of structures in high-risk areas. And, if complete withdrawal from high-risk areas is not possible, it is then important to employ earthquake-resistant construction techniques.

If an earthquake strikes your town, what you do during and immediately after the first tremor may make life-and-death differences for you. These earthquake safety rules suggested by the Environmental Science Services Administration will help you survive.

DURING THE SHAKING:

Don't panic. The motion is frightening but, unless it shakes something down on top of you, it is harmless. The earth does not yawn open, gulp down a neighborhood, and slam shut. Keep calm and ride it out.

If it catches you indoors, stay indoors. Take cover under a desk, table, bench, or in doorways, halls, and against side walls. Stay away from glass.

Don't use candles, matches, or other open flames, either during or after the tremor. Douse all fires.

If the earthquake catches you outside, move away from buildings and utility wires. Once in the open, stay there until the shaking stops.

Don't run through or near buildings. The greatest danger from falling debris is just outside doorways and close to outer walls.

If you are in a moving car, stop as quickly as safety permits, but stay in the vehicle. A car is an excellent seismometer, and will jiggle fearsomely on its springs during the earthquake; but it is a good place to stay until the shaking stops.

AFTER THE SHAKING:

Check your utilities, but do not turn them on. Earth movement may have cracked water, gas, and electrical conduits.

If you smell gas, open windows and shut off the main valve. Then leave the building and report gas leakage to authorities. Don't reenter the house until a utility official says it is safe.

If water mains are damaged, shut off the supply at the main valve.

If electrical wiring is shorting out, close the switch at the main meter box.

Turn on your radio or television (if conditions permit) to get the latest emergency bulletins.

Stay off the telephone except to report an emergency.

Don't go sight-seeing.

Stay out of severely damaged buildings; aftershocks can shake them down.

2. Volcanoes

The Kilauea volcano looks relatively peaceful after a night of wild eruption.

Lava from the eruption of the night before poured onto the roadway.

2. Volcanoes

It is Tuesday, August 5, 1969. The time is 9:30 P.M. The smell of sulfur dioxide, hydrogen sulfide, and other sulfur-bearing gases filling our nostrils is overpowering and makes breathing distasteful and painful. The awesome, crackling sound filling the air leaves no doubt in our minds that the surface of the earth is being ripped and torn. There before our eyes the darkness of the night is lit by a fire alternately exploding from and then ebbing into the earth. It is a spectacle that is hard to describe.

For more than eight hours the eruptions continue. At 6 A.M., things begin to quiet down. With the coming of the first light of dawn, we look off to the right and see a huge, massive mountain. Its top is snow-covered. A marker nearby carries the name *Mauna Loa*, elevation 13,680 feet above sea level.

No, we are not in a foreign country. We are in the United States and we have been watching a volcanic eruption for more than eight hours. And there, off to our right, *is* Mauna Loa—the world's largest single mountain and active volcano. Mauna Loa, of course, has been calm and silent since its last eruption in 1950 when lava flowing from it reached the sea on the west side of the island.

The eruption that held our attention for eight hours is the Kilauea volcano. It is the youngest of the five volcanoes that form the 4,000-square-mile island that is called Hawaii. During the 1960s, Kilauea erupted more than fourteen times. In fact, this volcano erupted more times in the 1960s than in any other decade of this century.

Hawaii, of course, is not the only state that harbors these fiery mountains. Mount Wrangell, for example, is an active volcano in the state of Alaska. It stands more than 14,000 feet above sea level, and it has been active in this century. There is an active volcano on the mainland of the United States, too. It is Lassen Peak, located in northeastern California. Lassen Peak stands 10,457 feet above sea level and is the most southerly major peak in the volcanic Cascade Range.

Lassen Peak is composed primarily of lava rocks. The oldest of these solidified two million years ago. Lassen Peak is a rare dome-type volcano. Its top was formed from thick viscous lavas. Another peak nearby called Cinder Cone was last active in 1851, and the peak called Chaos Crags is thought to be the result of volcanic activity in 1720.

Lassen Peak's eruptions in this century began without warning. Volcanic ash, steam, and lava were spewed forth on May 30, 1914. This activity continued in on-again, off-again fashion for a year. Then on May 19, 1915, the explosions became more violent and hot ejecta (cinders, ash, etc.) spilled 1,000 feet down the mountain. The last eruption of Lassen Peak occurred in 1921.

Lassen Peak erupted in 1915.

Now, we might take some comfort in the fact that for more than fifty years Lassen Peak has been quiet. Evidence, however, suggests there is a possibility of a sixty-five year cycle for volcanic activity in the Cascade Range. If this is true, then we might expect some activity in the mid-1980s.

Lassen Peak has never given us an awe-inspiring spectacle of a really violent outburst in this century. But before we become too comfortable, let's remember that on August 24 in the year 79 A.D. an apparently extinct volcano suddenly exploded and destroyed the Roman city of Pompeii. The volcano buried Pompeii so deeply under a deluge of ashes that it remained covered for 1,800 years.

The year 79 A.D. may seem to be much too remote to be used as an example. There is, however, an eyewitness report to that event. It was written by a young boy whose name was

Caius Pliny. In fact, Caius Pliny is referred to as "Pliny the Younger" to distinguish him from his uncle, "Pliny the Elder." Both Plinys were enthusiastic students of nature. The elder Pliny was so interested in the eruption that he tried to get as close as possible to make observations. He lost his life by suffocation in the hot, overpowering gases that came from the volcano. But Pliny the Younger survived the day and gave to science the first accurate written description of a volcanic eruption.

Today the volcano that is near the ancient city of Pompeii is called *Vesuvius*. It stands 4,000 feet high and is seven miles from the present Italian city of Naples. But in the first century A.D., this volcano did not exist as we know it today. There was, in fact, a much larger volcano there. It was called *Monte Somma*. At least eighty volcanic mountains the size of Vesuvius could have fit into Monte Somma.

The history of Monte Somma and the tragedy that befell Pompeii are interesting. In remote times, an enormous stream of lava descended from Monte Somma to the valley of the Sarno. The lava hardened and solidified. Over thousands of years, plants dug into the lava and entrenched themselves in what proved to be a very rich, hospitable environment. Then people moved in and occupied the area in about the eighth century B.C. And, for more than eight hundred years, a rich, flourishing culture and a number of cities developed in the shadow of the mountain.

If we had looked in on Monte Somma on that August day in 79 A.D., we would not have observed a volcanic cone at all. We would, in fact, have seen a great hollow valley surrounded by steep sloping cliffs. We would not have seen a cloud of steam coming from the mountain's top as we generally do when we observe Vesuvius today. The valley, on that day in August, was filled with green growing things. Plants, bushes, and small pine trees flourished. Monte Somma was not considered to be a volcano at all. The mountain, in the memory of all the

Plants begin to grow in lava a few years after it has cooled. This plant is actually four inches high.

people, had been nothing but a huge, hollow, harmless hill and everyone thought that it would go on being just that—if they thought about it at all.

Unknown to the citizens of Pompeii, Monte Somma was taking one of its "naps" and there were ominous signs that it was ready to wake up. Sixteen years before, in 63 A.D., for example, a succession of violent earthquakes shook the region.

41

In fact, the quakes continued intermittently for sixteen years right up until the year 79 A.D. But the people did not associate the quakes with Monte Somma until, on that fateful morning, a gigantic black cloud in the shape of a pine tree rose from the summit and Pompeii was buried. Thus, the life of Pompeii was "sandwiched" between two eruptions of Monte Somma. Within the space of a few short hours, eight centuries of man's efforts were wiped out. The huge destructive power that spews forth from the volcanoes of this earth is indeed awesome, and there seems to be no escape from the inevitable.

The typical picture of a volcano in action is one of streams of hot lava running over its top and down its sides. But, in the eruption of Monte Somma there was no overflow of melted lava. All the damage was caused by hardened masses of lava and ash that were blown out of the old crater. The hardened material was built up centuries before during previous eruptions of the volcano.

During the next twelve centuries, following the burial of Pompeii, eruptions occurred every fifty to one hundred years and the shape of Monte Somma gradually changed. From the thirteenth to the seventeenth century A.D., the eruptions became less frequent. In fact, there were only two outbursts over this span of four hundred years. But then in 1631, about ten years after the Pilgrims landed at Plymouth Rock, Mount Vesuvius erupted violently. It spewed lava and destruction and killed eighteen thousand people in the surrounding cities. And the mountain has had a conical shape ever since. It has never returned to the wide, cuplike valley which it had when it was known to the Romans as Monte Somma.

For the last three hundred years, Vesuvius has never really settled down. In fact, the eruptions have been so violent that the cone's top has been shattered and blown off in more than just a few of the eruptions. The cone, however, has always been built up again. In June, 1900, for example, Vesuvius swelled to a height of 4,275 feet; but then, after a tremendous eruption in 1906, it shrank to a height of 3,068 feet.

Vesuvius seems to follow a cycle of continuous filling in, swelling under confined pressure, exploding, and then collapsing. It seems to take about fifteen to twenty-five years to complete the cycle. The eruption of 1906 was followed by minor activity in 1913 and then a tremendous explosion in 1929. The cycle is due to natural forces within the earth which must play themselves out. A major eruption occurred in 1944, but one has not occurred since that date. At the present time, we are more than twenty-five years beyond the time of the last eruption. No one is quite sure when the next will occur or, for that matter, how violent it will be. This is a subject that should concern all of us. What causes a volcano to remain dormant for many years? What are the forces at work beneath the surface that suddenly cause it to burst and erupt?

Tremendous quantities of heat—generated by physical and chemical processes—exist deep within the earth. This heat is the key to the disruptive forces that produce volcanoes. It melts the rock in the upper part of the mantle, generates convection currents, and unleashes forces that work within and on the surface of the earth, causing the solid outer crust to develop weak spots, to shift, and to buckle. The cracks produced in the outer crust reach down toward the mantle. Hot, melted, gas-charged rock called *magma* moves into these cracks and works its way toward the surface. The molten, bubbling magma may eventually flood out onto the surface of the earth. It may flow quietly like thick honey, or it may burst through the crust with expansive force.

The magma contains entrapped gases which burst free as the molten rock reaches the surface. The violent spectacle that we associate with a volcanic eruption is created by the explosive force of these gases being released suddenly. The escaping gases are intensely hot and most are poisonous. Steam,

The lava is thick and viscous. It was still quite warm when the photograph was taken, the morning after the eruption.

carbon dioxide, carbon monoxide, hydrogen sulfide, sulfur dioxide, other sulfurous gases, hydrochloric acid, as well as hydrogen and nitrogen, are among the gases released by the magma.

When lava is at a temperature of 2,200° F, it flows readily and the entrapped gases escape easily. Eruptions produced at these temperatures are usually quiet and mild. This is the type of eruption that occurs on the island of Hawaii. The escaping gas throws the lava high into the sky. The eruption resembles a fountain of fire.

When the temperature of lava is below 2,000° F, it is very sticky or viscous. Entrapped gases have great difficulty in escaping from viscous lava. In such cases, the gases accumulate until their entrapped energy is sufficient to break through the encircling lava. Eruptions, under these circumstances, occur as a series of explosions. Stromboli is a volcano in the Lipari Islands north of Sicily whose eruptions are of this type.

In many cases, the mouth of a volcano becomes blocked by rock fragments or by a plug of solidified lava. Gases accumulate below the plug and build pressure. When the pressure builds sufficiently, the gases burst through the obstruction. Such an eruption, carrying with it huge clouds of steam together with other gases and chunks of solid rock, is frightening and, more often than not, very destructive. Vesuvius is an example of this type of eruption. The pressure of the gas below the clogged crater pushes the plug out like a cork escaping from a champagne bottle. Pent-up energy is released all at once.

Some of the water that produces the steam that accompanies volcanic eruptions comes from the same place as the magma. Another portion is picked up as the magma works its way to the surface. Water picked up by the magma en route is ordinary *ground water*. Ground water comes mostly from rain. The water, however, that comes from deep within the earth and has never been on the surface is called *juvenile water*. It is entirely probable that all the water on the surface, including ocean water, was initially brought up from the depths of the earth as juvenile water by volcanoes.

Vesuvius may seem remote to you. But there is a very tragic example—closer to home—of what can happen when a great plug blocks the vent of a volcano. The tragedy occurred on the island of Martinique in 1902. Mount Pelée, a volcano on this island in the West Indies, belched up ashes, mud, and sulfurous gases in 1851. Then, over the next fifty years, it showed no signs of being active; and some thirty thousand people moved into its shadow and settled down in the seaport of St. Pierre. This city was the capital of Martinique in 1902. Mount Pelée protected St. Pierre from the winds and storms which blew in from the Atlantic Ocean.

A crystal-clear lake filled the crater of Mount Pelée. In April, 1902, the lake suddenly disappeared from the crater and a huge cloud of smoke shot up from the mountain. Then, on May 5, a vent opened and a mixture of boiling mud and gas poured out and destroyed a sugar factory. Just as suddenly as it had opened, a collapse sealed the vent from which the boiling mud was flowing; and the townspeople relaxed.

Even a casual observer, however, could see that the whole mountain was beginning to bulge and swell. A great plug was blocking the central vent of Mount Pelée. Initially, the pressure below was not sufficient to blow out the plug, but it mounted day by day. The bulge continued to grow and to distort the shape of the mountain; still the pressure was not great enough to blow the plug or tear off the top of the volcano. Instead, the pressure caused the mountain to bulge to such an extent that the whole side facing St. Pierre gave way. A cloud of hot gas and fiery fragments roared toward the city. St. Pierre was struck by a huge hot belch of debris. The French on the island of Martinique, even today, refer to this hot debris, which had a temperature of 1,500° F, as a fiery cloud. Every building in the capital was destroyed and set ablaze. And the thirty thousand residents lost their lives. Only one man survived—a prisoner in a deep dungeon.

A volcano is the hill that develops around the vent or crack in the earth from which the lava flows. When lava oozes quietly from a hole, it tends to spread out and form a broad, gently-sloping shield. The islands of Hawaii are shield volcanoes. The base of each volcano rests on the floor of the Pacific Ocean. Lava flowing quietly from the cracks at the bottom of the sea gradually built until the mass of rock rose above the surface of the sea.

The Hawaiian Islands appear as tiny dots on a map of the Pacific Ocean. But they are, in reality, the tops of a range of mighty mountains. Thousands upon thousands of volcanic eruptions, each contributing a thin lava flow, have added to the

People rebuilt the town of St. Pierre. Mount Pelée dominates the small fishing village, and it still provides protection from Atlantic winds.

accumulation that built up from the sea floor. The average depth of the floor of the Pacific Ocean in the vicinity of the Hawaiian Islands is 15,000 feet. Thus, when the first of these islands pushed above the surface of the sea, it was a mountain more than 15,000 feet high. Mauna Kea, a volcano on the island of Hawaii, rises more than 30,000 feet above its base.

The line of islands that we call the state of Hawaii stretches 1,500 miles across the central Pacific. The oldest rocks presently above sea level are probably ten million years old. The building force of volcanism met very little opposition as long as the flow of lava was beneath the surface of the sea. But as the top of the volcanoes pushed toward the sea surface, currents and then waves began to attack the growing mass of frozen lava. The currents and waves loosened and washed away fragments of the lava rock. As the volcanoes pushed above the sea, a more in-

We are on the "Big Island" of Hawaii in the city of Hilo. The volcanic peaks are in the background. More often than not, they are enshrouded in clouds and completely hidden from view.

tense attack began. The destructive forces of wind, wave, and water erosion carved away the rock. But as long as lava poured from the vents of the volcanoes, the islands continued to grow.

The forces of erosion seized control on some of the islands when volcanic activity died out. Streams carved canyons and cut high cliffs into the slopes. Then, at some time in the distant past, corals moved onto the submerged platforms that formed the slopes of the Hawaiian volcanoes. These tiny organisms secreted limy skeletons and formed reefs. Today, we can find reefs called *fringing reefs* surrounding each central volcanic island.

The volcanic activity of the Hawaiian Islands proceeded southeastward. The volcanoes at the northwestern end of the chain stopped erupting long before those on the southeastern end. In fact, some of the volcanic mountains at the northwestern end have been eroded away until no volcanic rock can be seen. Midway Island is an example in which a volcanic island has entirely disappeared leaving only its limestone reef projecting slightly above the water. Thus, the visible part of Midway Island is formed entirely of organic limestone and calcareous sand. But, at a depth of a few hundred feet, the limestone rests on the summit of a great volcanic mountain.

The island of Hawaii is the southernmost and largest of the Hawaiian Islands. It is also the youngest island in the chain. Five great volcanoes actually built the island of Hawaii. Kohala volcano, at the northern end of the island, is the oldest of the volcanoes. Huge canyons have been cut into its rainy northeastern slope by streams. Waves driven by the trade winds have cut high cliffs into the northeastern shore. Mauna Kea probably had its last eruption some fifteen thousand years ago. Hualalai, on the western part of the island, erupted for the last time in 1801. But the two southernmost volcanoes, Mauna Loa and Kilauea, are still active and put on some spectacular shows. In fact, Mauna Loa and Kilauea are so active that erosion has had very little opportunity to mar their surfaces.

In some areas of the earth, lava flows from very long cracks in the crust. When this occurs, the lava spreads out evenly in all directions. Extensive lava plains or plateaus form in this way. The Columbia River plateau in northwestern United States is an example of a lava plain. The actual eruption of the lava in these cases occurs very quickly. The flow is rapid and extensive. More than 100,000 square miles, for example, were covered by lava to form the Columbia Plateau in what is now eastern Washington and Idaho.

The depth of the lava in these plateaus may reach a thickness of 5,000 feet. The Deccan of central India is a notable example of a lava plateau. The only record of an eruption of this type, witnessed by man, occurred in Iceland. This was the Laki fissure eruption that took place in 1783. Twenty-two separate vents along a ten-mile length of the fissure poured out lava.

The molten rock flowed for a distance of fifty miles. The average depth of the lava in the Laki fissure eruption is 100 feet. But some valleys, it should be noted, were filled to a depth of 600 feet.

Lava remains hot even after it has begun to freeze and solidify. A lava flow which is 300 feet thick, for example, may take thirty years to cool from 2,000° to 1,100° F. At a temperature of 2,000° F, lava gives off a yellow glow. At 1,100°, lava appears dull red. Lava varies greatly in its chemical composition. Only the solid material that is left after it has cooled and hardened is taken into consideration in determining its chemical composition. After all, it is very difficult to capture and analyze a sample of magma complete with its entrapped gases. Thus, scientists tend to disregard the gases in making a chemical analysis.

Silicon dioxide is the most abundant substance in lava. Generally, the amount of silica ranges from 40 to 75 per cent. As the percentage of silica increases, there is a corresponding increase in the amount of alkalis such as sodium and potassium oxides. On the other hand, as the percentage of silica decreases, there is an increase in the oxides of iron, magnesium, and calcium. The oxides of aluminum, titanium, phosphorus, and magnesium are also found in lava. The gases found in lava usually include water vapor as steam, carbon dioxide, carbon monoxide, hydrogen, nitrogen, argon, sulfur dioxide, sulfur trioxide, sulfur, and chlorine.

Magma often supplies the heat that maintains geysers, hot springs, steam vents, and mud pots. In geysers, for example, the heated water generally occupies a vertical tube that has an opening at ground level. The bottom layer of the water in the vertical tube boils at a higher temperature than the water at the top because the bottom section is under greater pressure. When the water at the bottom begins to boil, it rises toward the surface. As it moves upward, there is a reduction in pressure which causes the superheated water to flash into steam. The steam

This dormant volcano, Fujiyama, is the highest mountain in Japan, rising 12,388 feet. It is admired for its graceful symmetry and majestic beauty.

that forms has a volume many times greater than the water it replaces. Thus, the water content of the geyser tube is squirted out when steam forms. One of the famous examples of a geyser is "Old Faithful" in Yellowstone National Park.

A volcano built of nothing but solid fragments is called a *cinder cone*. Cinder cones are among the smallest volcanoes. They have steep sides and a narrow base. Cinder cones usually form when large amounts of escaping gas break the lava into a frothy broth. The broth forms a fine spray which solidifies rapidly. Under these conditions, little or no lava flows as a liquid.

Volcanoes are not entirely of one type; that is, they are not exclusively cinder cones, nor exclusively shield volcanoes. Most volcanoes are a little of each. They are, in fact, composites of fragmental material and lava. This means they sometimes erupt quietly and at other times explosively. The eruptions that build composite cones usually begin with explosions of solid material from the crater. These explosions are then followed by lava flowing through fissures in the sides of the mountain. Mount Fujiyama in Japan is an example of a perfectly formed composite cone.

Scientists need to learn more about volcanoes. These fiery mountains are windows that allow us to peer into the earth's crust. There are volcano observatories throughout the world. The United States Geological Survey maintains a volcano observatory in Kilauea, Hawaii. Studies have been made for more than fifty years on the Kilauea volcano; measurements of the temperature and pressure of the gas are made. In addition, the scientists keeping the diary of Kilauea's activities sample the lava in the rocks. They also study the magnetic field of the volcano. Knowledge and understanding are necessary if we are to accurately predict when eruptions are likely to occur. Thus, the immediate, practical goal of these studies is to predict the time and type of eruptions. When we can make these predictions with a degree of accuracy, it will help to reduce the terrible toll of life and property taken by these natural disasters.

The next step after prediction is to struggle with the problem of control. It is highly unlikely that we will be able to change the inside of the earth or to modify the forces that produce volcanoes. But it is highly probable that with better insight we may be able to control lava flows and mud flows. We may also be able to tap the heat and the steam generated by volcanoes to heat homes and to produce electricity.

3. Thunderstorms

Cumulus clouds.

3. Thunderstorms

A devastating storm slashed across northern Ohio driving hundred-mile-an-hour winds before it. July 4 celebrations in Cleveland were disrupted when it struck a mere seven minutes after a severe thunderstorm warning was issued. The story of the tragedy produced by the storm was still being written on July 5, 1969, as U.S. coastguardsmen battled high winds and choppy waters in a search for two hundred persons missing on Lake Erie.

Most of us, at one time or another, have had a walk, picnic, or an outing interrupted by a thunderstorm. Lightning, hail, and torrential rains are the most destructive products of these storms that strike in spring and summer. As the thunderstorm advances, the driving wind bends tree branches and causes huge waves to develop in lakes and rivers. From out of the heavy masses of clouds, with their great vertical development, awesome bolts of lightning send fiery fingers toward the earth. To an observer on the ground the clouds appear to be mountainous.

The upper parts of the clouds have a fibrous texture, and they often spread out in the shape of an anvil. The fury of a thunderstorm never ceases to be frightening no matter how many times you experience it. The sheer power of the crop-destroying hail and the torrential rains can overwhelm you. The lightning bolts can kill, and the heavy rains exact a toll from the earth itself as they wash tons of soil into streams and rivers and on into the sea.

Until very recently, no one really knew what went on inside a thundercloud. Very few people, after all, had ever been inside one. But during the 1960s, scientists probed these clouds. Airplanes, balloons, and other devices were used to collect data. The information gathered indicates that there are three distinct stages to the development of a thunderstorm. We can refer to these stages as birth, maturity, and death.

Fleecy white cumulus clouds are usually a sign of fair weather. But it is from a cumulus cloud slowly drifting across the sky on a warm day that a thunderstorm is born. In order for this birth to occur, however, certain essential conditions must be met: First, there must be a large surface area with a huge supply of moist air hovering above. The second condition is that there should be little or no wind. Wind, after all, keeps the atmosphere stirred. It discourages local overheating; and local overheating is another of the primary conditions to be met.

The sun supplies the impulse that changes the cumulus cloud into a cumulonimbus cloud or thunderhead. The energy of the sun is absorbed by the surface of the ground which, in turn, radiates energy that heats the underside of the air mass immediately above. This causes the layer of air in contact with the warm surface to expand. But it does not expand as a huge mass. The air warmed in this way breaks up into cells and then pockets of expanding air move through the center of the cells.

The anvil of a huge cumulonimbus cloud reaches skyward.

As the expanding air rises, its temperature is lowered. The cooling leads to condensation which, in turn, liberates heat. Under the proper circumstances, enough heat is liberated to keep the convection system operating and to propel the air to a height of four or five miles.

The birth of the thunderstorm starts with the upward expansion of moist air. This initial stage is sometimes referred to as the cumulus stage. The strong updraft that develops within a cumulus cloud forms the thunderhead, or towering anvil, of a cumulonimbus cloud. The upward-moving, or ascending, currents attain speeds of one hundred feet per second, or more than sixty miles per hour.

Cloud droplets condense and grow within the updraft. Some of these raindrops fall down through the cloud. As the water vapor cools and condenses into droplets, heat is released. And it is this heat that adds more power and lift to the updraft. The powerful updrafts cause great quantities of water vapor to be carried aloft.

Huge B-57 aircraft have been outfitted as flying research laboratories by ESSA to probe the mysteries of the storms produced by our atmosphere.

In the upper frigid heights of the cloud, the water vapor condenses into tiny ice crystals, which collide with other ice crystals and with snowflakes. Layer upon layer freezes around the crystals until sizable hailstones are built. The droplets that remain in the lower regions of the cumulonimbus cloud join to form larger raindrops.

The mature stage begins when the accumulation of ice crystals, water drops, or hailstones in the upper region of the cloud exceeds the weight that can be supported by the updraft. It is at this point that a sudden change takes place in the circulation of the air within the cumulonimbus cloud. Water drops, ice particles, and hailstones begin to fall through the less vigorous currents in the outer region of the cloud and a cool downdraft forms. At this stage, a warm updraft and a cool downdraft exist side by side.

As the downdraft moves through the cloud, it carries raindrops, ice drops, and hailstones along with it. When the downdraft breaks through the lower portion of the cloud, it streaks toward the earth. As it approaches the surface, it spreads out laterally. The downdraft is colder than the updraft that started the process. Thus, the downdraft has the quality of a cold air mass as it moves out laterally along the earth's surface.

The leading edge of the downdraft behaves just like a miniature cold front. It produces gusts of wind that can develop into a squall. The cool downdraft also causes a sudden drop in temperature as it moves over the surface. The temperature may, in fact, drop as much as ten degrees. A downpour of rain or, at times, hail usually follows the drop in temperature.

A thunderstorm produced in this way lasts for about fifteen or thirty minutes. It builds quickly and becomes very intense. Thunder and lightning often accompany the precipitation.

The downdraft and the precipitation cool the ground below. In fact, if the downdraft is a strong one the resulting flow of cold air will undercut the zone of updraft. Once the updraft is reduced, the supply of moisture being carried upward decreases and the third stage in the life cycle of the thunderstorm begins. It is then only a matter of time before the storm withers and dies because it is deprived of fresh supplies of moist, rising air.

As the thunderhead loses its water-drop content, the large-scale, vertical movement of air, both upward and downward, comes to an end. Cutting off its water supply stops the process of condensation and the thunderstorm's power dwindles and dissipates rapidly. Rainfall, lightning, and thunder fade away and the temperature within the cloud gradually changes to that of the surrounding air.

It is rather obvious that the onset of maturity that begins with the formation of the downdraft spells disaster for the thunderstorm. No individual storm can last for more than an hour. But taken in a broader sense, thunderstorm activity does continue for more than an hour in some instances. What apparently happens is that the outflowing current of cold air triggers a new updraft in the vicinity of the one it destroys. The triggering of a new updraft is most likely to occur when two cold outflows from mature thunderheads collide. In a number of instances, the new updraft develops even before there has been time for the cold downdraft to make its influence felt.

A single thunderhead can sprawl over an area of several hundred square miles. The peaks of these clouds may tower to 40,000 feet. And the storms which reach out from these billowy masses can occur in lines as long as 300 miles. These cumulonimbus clouds are not stationary. They move across country at 13 to 35 miles per hour.

Turbulence within the thunderhead is not uniform. There is much less in the lower levels of the cloud, that is, below 10,000 feet. The greatest turbulence occurs between 15,000 and 20,000 feet. These elevations are considered to be the middle altitudes within the cloud. The hail and lightning hazards are greatest at these intermediate levels, too.

Heat is one of the triggers for the three-stage development of a thunderstorm because the earth's surface absorbs and reflects the sun's energy at varying rates. At the beach, for example,

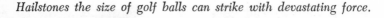

Hailstones the size of golf balls can strike with devastating force.

there are really two kinds of surfaces absorbing and reflecting energy. One is the water surface of the ocean; the other is the sandy area that lines the shore. The same quantity of energy falls on both surfaces, that is, the water and the sand. Water, however, has a great heat capacity and can absorb huge quantities of energy without having its temperature affected. Sand, on the other hand, absorbs the energy and goes through a rapid increase in temperature during the day.

The water temperature of the ocean may start out in the morning at 75° F. The sand may be at approximately the same temperature during the morning. But by midafternoon, sand temperatures may soar forty degrees or more, while the water temperature may not vary by more than one degree Fahrenheit. In such an instance, the air over the sand may be heated sufficiently to produce an updraft or convection current.

Convection, remember, is a process of heat or energy transfer. The hot sand transfers energy to the lower layers of the air above it. The air expands, decreases in density, and rises in an upward current. As the warm air over the land rises, moist, cooler air moves in from the sea and takes its place. It is usual for the breeze to blow from the sea toward the land during the day. We call this movement of air a "sea" breeze. As the sea air moves over the land, it receives and absorbs energy from the hot sand and, as a consequence, heats up and rises.

Remember, clouds are simply parcels of air that have been lifted high enough to condense the water vapor they contain into very small visible drops. The inner cloud particles are too small to drop out and fall as rain, but as the lifting process continues these water drops grow in size by collision and accumulation. *Cumulus* means accumulation, and a cumulus cloud gets its start in response to the updrafts created by the variation of the way in which sand and water absorb and reflect solar radiation.

The seacoast thunderstorm is classified as a local air-mass thunderstorm. It is most often an isolated convective storm that has been triggered by heat. All air-mass thunderstorms are local or heat thunderstorms in origin.

We often associate the distant rumble of a thunderstorm with a mountain range or hills. The mountain thunderstorm is produced when warm, moist air is driven to higher altitudes as it strikes a mountain barrier. The mountain serves mechanically to elevate winds as they blow across the land. The mechanical lifting of the warm, moist air is given an added impetus by up-drafts rising from the sun-warmed slopes. Many of the thunderstorms that occur in the Rocky Mountain states are brought about by this combination of events.

Another group of these storms is referred to as *frontal* thunderstorms. Basically, there are two kinds: a cold-front thunderstorm and a warm-front thunderstorm. A weather front is defined as the area in which two air masses, one cold and the other warm, meet and clash. The terms *warm* and *cold* are used in a relative way by meteorologists. When considering any two air masses, the one with the higher temperature is referred to as warm, while the other is said to be cold. In a situation in which a cold air mass is advancing and pushing against a warm air mass, we refer to the front as a cold front. A warm front is one in which a warm air mass is advancing and rising up and over a colder air mass.

A cold-front thunderstorm may develop when a wedge of cold air pushes into and under a mass of warm air. In such a situation, warm air is lifted aloft. If there is sufficient moisture in the warm air, condensation may occur and huge cumulus clouds may develop. If conditions are right, these clouds may develop into cumulonimbus clouds and produce a thunderstorm. A line of cold-front thunderstorms can extend for hundreds of miles along the advancing edge of a cold front.

Thunderstorms are produced less often by advancing warm fronts than by advancing cold fronts. But, nevertheless, they are produced often enough for the meteorologist to keep a wary eye on the situation. An advancing warm front means that warm air is pushing up and over a retreating wedge of cold air. The vertical slope along which the warm air rides up and over the cold air is usually not very steep. Thus, the uplift of air is slow and gradual. Warm-front thunderstorms are usually less severe than cold-front thunderstorms. Much of the action of a warm-front thunderstorm takes place far above an obscuring layer of clouds.

In any event, in both types of frontal thunderstorms—that is, cold and warm—a pattern is created as warm, moist air is driven skyward. Once the warm, moist air starts to move upward, the three-stage development of a thunderstorm has a chance to complete its cycle. Frontal thunderstorms are common in the Midwest.

In the first of the three stages, an expanding cumulus cloud may be a mile in diameter and stretch some 15,000 feet high. Even if the surface temperature is in the low eighties, the temperature at an altitude of 15,000 feet will be about 32° F. In approximately ten minutes, the expanding cumulus cloud can swell to a diameter of five to ten miles; and its upper portion can be at an altitude of 40,000 feet. At this point, it is a fully developed cumulonimbus cloud. The base of one of these thunderheads may be some 500 to 13,000 feet above the earth's surface. At altitudes of 40,000 feet, the temperatures range around −60° F. The upper levels of these clouds are quite cold.

The energy contained in an average thunderstorm is almost unbelievable. There is, of course, no way of measuring it accurately. But the best estimates that scientists can make indicate that an average thunderstorm can release more energy in one minute than a 120-kiloton nuclear bomb. It is sufficient to say that the potential for destruction in one of these storms is tremendous.

Thunderstorms can develop almost anywhere. Evidence indicates that each year approximately sixteen million thunderstorms are spawned throughout the world. This is a fantastic

Wave action is always destructive, but waves whipped by storms are devastating to small craft.

number. It means that, at any given moment, assuming equal distribution in time, there are two thousand thunderstorms in some stage of development.

Meteorological records indicate that Kampala, Uganda, has about 242 days during which thunderstorms occur each year. This means that there are storms on an average of at least twenty days of each month. The island of Java is another location that has a high average. There are 223 thunderstorm days a year in Java.

A belt along the equator is noted for its low pressure and is referred to as the *Doldrum Belt*. The temperatures in the Doldrums are consistently high, and there is plenty of moist air. People living in the Doldrum Belt usually experience 75 to 150 thunderstorm days a year.

Looking at the earth as a whole, we can identify certain regions in which thunderstorms are a rare occurrence. Generally, these locations in both hemispheres lie between the poles and the 60° latitude line. The 60° N latitude line cuts through the Hudson Bay area of Canada. The air over this region of the earth is much too cold and generally too stable to allow thunderstorms to develop. In addition, the energy of the sun does not heat the earth sufficiently to generate the convection system necessary to brew a thunderstorm.

North of the Arctic Circle the air is cold and quite dry. Thunderstorms occur in this region very infrequently; possibly one may occur every few years.

There are also locations between the 60° latitude line and the equator where the right combination of conditions does not occur. In desert areas, for example, in the low latitudes, there is sufficient heat but not enough moisture to stoke and brew a thunderstorm. Thus, thunderstorms occur only about five days of the year in these low latitude desert areas.

There are practically no areas in the United States that are free from thunderstorms and the hazards that accompany them. Most of Alaska, of course, is above the 60° N latitude line. The thunderstorm days, that is, the days on which thunderstorms are brewed in Alaska, are less than ten per year. Hawaii also has a frequency of less than ten. The coastal areas along the Pacific, that is, the extreme western portions of Washington, Oregon, and California, have a thunderstorm frequency of less than five days a year, while the Gulf Coast of Florida has a frequency of more than ninety days. There is one section of south central Florida that has a frequency of one hundred thunderstorm days a year.

Over practically the whole of Canada and the Pacific slopes of the Rockies, the frequency is less than twenty. Most of the New England states, including the eastern portion of New York State, most of New Jersey, Delaware, and the extreme eastern portion of Maryland, average from twenty to thirty thunderstorm days per year. The eastern portion of Maine averages below twenty. For most of Pennsylvania, a small section of northwestern New Jersey, and the southern portion of New York State that borders Pennsylvania, the frequency of thunderstorm days is between thirty and forty.

The extreme eastern portion of Virginia has a frequency of less than forty. The central portion of Virginia has a frequency of less than fifty, whereas the extreme southwestern tip of Virginia experiences between fifty and sixty thunderstorm days per year.

North Carolina, approximately from Winston-Salem eastward to Cape Hatteras, experiences about fifty thunderstorm days per year. The remainder of the state west of Winston-Salem has a frequency of approximately sixty. Tennessee, most of South Carolina, Georgia, Alabama, Mississippi, Arkansas, Missouri, the extreme western section of Illinois, the extreme southern section of Iowa, most of Kansas, Oklahoma, and the extreme eastern portion of Texas also have a frequency of about sixty thunderstorm days per year.

As you approach the southeastern border of the eastern United States, the thunderstorm risk increases. For example, as you move from northern Georgia to southern Georgia, the frequency climbs from sixty to seventy thunderstorm days per year. A frequency belt of seventy moves from the extreme southern portion of South Carolina to Savannah, Georgia, through Waycross, Georgia, westward across southern Alabama then across central Mississippi through Meridian and westward to Vicksburg, and on through Monroe, Louisiana, westward to Shreveport, Louisiana, then turns south moving along the western border of Louisiana and the eastern border of Texas to Port Arthur.

In the United States, thunderstorms are most likely to occur in the areas frequented by maritime tropical air that originates either over the Gulf of Mexico or over the Gulf Stream. This maritime tropical air characteristically moves in toward the southeastern coast, striking the southern borders of Texas, Louisiana, Mississippi, Florida, and Georgia. It also sweeps in toward the west coast of Florida. Thus, the Tampa area and areas south of Tampa have a high thunderstorm frequency.

The Pikes Peak region of Colorado stands out as the one region in the West that has a high frequency. In fact, this is one of the few places in the United States where thunderstorms seem to be conspicuously more frequent on high ground than on low ground. The frequency approaches seventy thunderstorm days per year in the Pikes Peak region.

In the United States as a whole, July is easily the most thundery month. In fact, there are usually more thunderstorms in July than in all the other eleven months put together. There are exceptions to this rule, however, June, for example, is the month of maximum frequency in most of the Pacific Northwest, while May leads in Texas and central California. In southern California, March and April lead all the other months in thunderstorm frequency. Farther north, in the San Francisco area, December, February, and June are the leading months for thunderstorm activity.

But, generally speaking, the season of most heat—that is, summer, or the July period—is the season in which we can generally expect the most thunderstorm activity in the United States. There are only a few exceptions, primarily in California. In the case of southern California, the dryness of the summer air prevents any convection current from building a tower of cumulus clouds. There is a weather station located on Mount Tamalpais just north of San Francisco. In seventeen years, this station has recorded twenty-nine days with thunderstorms. This gives an average of less than two days per year.

An interesting fact is that in at least half the states more than 50 per cent of the summer thunderstorms occur between the hours of noon and 6 P.M. In the southeastern United States, less than 20 per cent of the summer storms occur between 6 P.M. and midnight.

The frequency with which thunderstorms occur throughout the United States and the quantity of energy they release make these storms great destroyers of life and property. The conditions which give rise to a major thunderstorm may also generate tornadoes and hail. Lightning, high winds, and heavy rains are part of any thunderstorm.

Meteorologists can predict the frontal type of storm quite accurately. They make their predictions by charting the large masses of warm and cold air that move back and forth across the country. The heat-type thunderstorm, however, is the result of more local conditions, and it is more difficult to forecast. But great progress has been made in predicting these air-mass thunderstorms, too.

ESSA, the Evironmental Science Services Administration, keeps a round-the-clock, round-the-calendar watch on atmospheric conditions. This organization provides routine forecasts for the United States, provides timely warning of severe storms, and also publishes thunderstorm safety rules. There are six of them. *Review these rules.* Make sure you understand them and prepare to act on the basis of the information that you receive:

Keep an eye on the weather during warm periods and during the passage of cold fronts. When cumulus clouds begin building up and darkening, you are probably in for a thunderstorm. Check the latest weather forecast.

Keep calm. Thunderstorms are usually of short duration; even squall lines pass in a matter of a few hours. Be cautious, but don't be afraid. Stay indoors and keep informed.

Know what the storm is doing. Remember that the mature stage may be marked on the ground by a sudden reversal of wind direction, a noticeable rise in wind speed, and a sharp drop in

68

temperature. Heavy rain, hail, tornadoes, and lightning generally occur only in the mature stage of the thunderstorm.

When conditions favor tornado formation, tune in your radio or television receiver to determine whether ESSA has a tornado watch or tornado warning out for your area. A tornado watch means one has been sighted or radar-indicated in your area. If you receive a tornado warning, *seek inside shelter in a storm cellar, below ground level, or in reinforced concrete structures; stay away from windows.*

Lightning is the thunderstorm's worst killer. Stay indoors and away from electrical appliances while the storm is overhead. If lightning catches you outside, remember that it seeks the easiest—not necessarily the shortest—distance between positive and negative centers. Keep yourself lower than the nearest highly conductive object, and maintain a safe distance from it. If the object is a tree, twice its height is considered a safe distance.

Thunderstorm rain may produce flash floods. Stay out of dry creek beds during thunderstorms. If you live along a river, listen for ESSA's flash flood warning.

4. Thunder, Lightning, and Havoc

An active fire in the Boise National Forest rapidly consumes the trees in its path.

4. Thunder, Lightning, and Havoc

Fires crackled across fifty miles of brush and dry grass in San Diego County on August 23, 1969. Crews from city fire departments, as well as state and federal forestry camps, worked in 100° heat to cut lines around the fires. In all, some seven hundred men battled the rampaging fires that blackened more than 50,000 acres and forced four hundred persons to flee their homes.

With all the havoc and destruction, the people in the area counted themselves lucky since the fires were burning away from populated areas. But many days passed before the fires were brought under control.

The biggest fire in the county was at Camp Pendleton. The site at which it started was fifteen miles southeast of San Clemente. The blaze burned and blackened 23,000 acres of the Camp Pendleton Marine Base and surrounding areas. Then it jumped into Cleveland National Forest and destroyed another 6,000 acres of timber.

Another fire burned alongside the Cleveland blaze and destroyed 15,000 acres in the Fall Brook–Temecula area. For a time, fire fighters feared that the blazes in the Cleveland National Forest and the Fall Brook–Temecula area would join.

At the same time, the Escondido area was being ravaged by still another fire. The location of this blaze was about ninety miles south of Los Angeles. More than 6,000 acres were charred and the walls of several luxury homes were blackened. Another holocaust flared near El Cajon, completely destroying ninety acres and six homes.

Fires sweeping across timber and grasslands, are a frightening spectacle. Tremendous losses are sustained in timber and property; and the time and energy of many men is required to control them. But when they move into an area in which people live, not only property but lives are in danger.

Lightning causes more than thirteen thousand forest fires each year in the United States. We are, of course, not the only country that suffers loss of life and property as a result of such natural disasters. While the fires were raging in San Diego County in 1969, a bolt of lightning turned a petroleum tank farm near Rome's International Airport into an inferno. Officials at the Italian installation said lightning cracked the concrete cap of a giant tank containing crude oil. The huge discharge of electricity ignited the oil with a blast that broke windows throughout the neighborhood. Flames spread to three of the other fifteen reservoirs in the installation. Fortunately, the tank farm was located on a man-made island in the Tiber River five miles from the Mediterranean Sea. But even in the limited area of the island, the inferno raged out of control and caused tremendous destruction.

Research going back to 1962 indicates that the blankets of small debris on forest floors actually spreads a forest fire. If the floors of the nation's forests could be tidied with a giant vacuum

A burned-over area is barren and desolate.

cleaner, the tremendous losses sustained each year could be cut dramatically. It is the blanket of small twigs, pine needles, and other debris that creates the favorable conditions for the thirteen thousand blazes that char the American forests every year. Included with the twigs and pine needles are dried grass, leaves, and lichens.

When lightning hits the top of a tree, the fire usually travels down the trunk and then spreads along the ground. But then, as the fire gets rolling—stoked by the debris—it consumes the tallest tree almost as fast as the smallest needle. Tidying the floors of the nation's forests may not be the best solution to follow, however. The small twigs, pine needles, lichens, dried grass, and leaves on the ground serve a purpose in the ecological scheme. Springtails, as one example, feed on various materials found on the forest floor. Recent research has shown that these small insects gorge themselves on the fruit of lichens, fungi, and other small plants. If we destroy the debris on the floors of the nation's forests, we would certainly disrupt the springtail communities. These insect communities are a part of a balance in nature that

Seeding is an effective way of "punching" holes in clouds.

we do not fully understand. At the present time, we need to keep all avenues of action opened to us. We must somehow proceed cautiously and assess the consequences of alternative plans for solving such problems.

Much of the present effort to control and prevent forest fires is directed skyward, that is, to the clouds and to the thunderheads in which lightning spawns. Programs of cloud seeding have been undertaken in the hope that such action will dissipate the energy within the huge thunderheads. A chemical called *silver iodide* is used to seed the clouds. These silver iodide particles spark the development of ice crystals, which help to drain off the electric charge from the cloud before it builds sufficiently to form a lightning stroke.

The program of cloud seeding has met with some success. As long ago as 1967, ESSA scientists found that seeding does reduce the number of lightning strokes from clouds. The experimenters also used tiny metallized nylon needles about five inches long as seed. Evidence indicates that metallic particles, as well as chemicals, can be used to prevent the build-up of the tremendous electrical charge required for a lightning stroke.

Many meteorologists, however, are still very skeptical about planned weather control. All the electricity produced in the United States in one day, for example, is just about equal to the energy of one large thunderstorm. Unless some simple trigger can be discovered to release the tremendous quantity of energy within a thunderhead, effective control may be out of the question.

The development of a simple trigger that can lead to effective control means that, first of all, we must understand the mechanics of a thunderstorm. Part of the problem, of course, is to learn more about the way in which the electrical charge builds. In order to attack this problem of getting more and better information, new devices had to be invented. In 1967, for example, a radar device called a *sferics-to-radar converter* was used for the first time to spot and rate lightning. The radar device pinpoints lightning areas within storms and also indicates the lightning intensity. The device was developed at the University of Miami's Radar Meteorological Laboratory.

The sferics-to-radar converter has a number of potential uses. The device can guide airline pilots around potential danger spots, for example. It can also be used to alert forest rangers of approaching fire danger. The instrument, as it was initially developed in 1967, consisted of one hundred transistors that collect radio noises emanating from electrical storms and convert them into arrow-like markings on a radar screen. These markings point to the zones of strongest electrical activity and also indicate their relative intensity.

Anyone who has witnessed a thunderstorm and has seen streaks of lightning cutting across the sky cannot help but be awe-stricken. Fear comes to the bravest person when lightning

Sferics-to-radar display.

strikes nearby, and he feels the charged air, sees the flash, and hears the crack and concussion of the thunder.

Remember, there are some two thousand thunderstorms in progress over the earth's surface at any given moment. It has been estimated that lightning strikes the earth on the average of one hundred times each second. Put this information together with the fact that the average annual death toll caused by lightning is greater than the death toll caused by tornadoes or hurricanes, and you begin to sense the dimensions of this type of natural disaster. On the average, about 150 deaths per year are caused by lightning. There are also approximately 250 additional people injured by these bolts of electricity which streak from the sky. Property loss as a result of fire and direct damage to structures, animals, and forests is estimated at more than $100 million annually.

Lightning, of course, is not an isolated phenomenon. It is an effect that results from the events that spawn a thunderstorm. Recall that updrafts of warm, moist air cause small cumulus clouds to grow into large cumulonimbus cloud systems. It is from these cumulonimbus clouds that the thunderstorm develops and the lightning is released. The puzzle is how the small cumulus cloud, as it makes its transition to the turbulent cumulonimbus giant, produces the gigantic electrical charge that streaks out of it as lightning. This is a puzzle which has not been solved.

The scientist uses hypotheses and theories to unlock the puzzles that perplex him. Here is a simple analogy used by some scientists to help explain the mystery of lightning. Thunderclouds, they say, generate electricity much as power stations do. These scientists view a cumulonimbus cloud as a kind of wind-driven dynamo. The difficulty for scientists is not to discover a suitable mechanism by which clouds and rain become electrified, but rather to identify the most significant way from among a number of possible ways they believe the raindrops or ice crystals can be charged. They hypothesize that there are at least three ways for charging to occur:

The impact of ice particles and supercooled water droplets upon pellets of soft hail can produce considerable electrification.

The breakup of raindrops can produce electrification. When water falls through a rising column of air, the larger drops split into smaller drops. The larger of these drops will possess a positive electrical charge. The smaller drops acquire negative charges. Remember that thunderclouds form at the tops of large rising air currents. The smaller particles that acquire a negative charge will be carried upward by the rising air. These particles will grow in size and then fall and separate again. Thus, a constant process of charging takes place within the turbulent cumulonimbus cloud.

The potential of a cloud can increase simply as a result of the constant turbulence taking place within it. As the potential

builds, the influence of the electrical field can cause other parti-
cles within the cloud to pick up positive and negative charges.

The first of these possibilities can be used to explain the negative charges found in the upper parts of clouds where the temperature is below the freezing point. The second and third of these explanations may account for the charges located in the lower atmosphere where the temperature is above freezing. All of these mechanisms may contribute to the charges found in precipitation when it reaches the ground. But much to the puzzlement of scientists studying the problem, none of these mechanisms nor any combination of them is capable of explaining the positive electricity invariably found in steady, light, or moderate rain.

The fact of the matter is that the mechanisms at work inside the thunderhead cause a piling up of negative electrical charges in one part of the cloud and of positive charges in another. This accumulation of charges is continued until the electrical attraction between the positive and negative charges becomes so great that a dart of electrons moves between them.

The dart, or movement, of electrons temporarily destroys the insulating property of the air along the discharge channel. This rush of current generates light, heat, and sound. Radio waves are also sent out by the electrical discharge. The radio waves created during thunderstorm activity are heard on our radio receivers as static. The interference range of these lightning-produced radio waves can be as great as 3,000 miles. Lightning discharges originating in the Doldrum Belt near the equator, for example, have been known to disturb radio reception as far away as Norway.

The electrical generating capacity of a thunderhead is fantastic. A single flash of lightning develops a million times the voltage used in ordinary house wiring. The flashes, of course, vary in the power they transmit and also in the voltage, or push, behind them. But it is not unusual for a cloud emitting a flash

A flash of lightning.

every ten seconds to develop about one million kilowatts. It takes the generating capacity of almost all the dams across the Tennessee Valley to produce this much power.

When we have finished with all the theory and speculation about how the wind-driven dynamo generates its electricity, the fact remains that an excess of electrons gathers at the base of the giant thunderhead. Thus, there is a strong negative charge at the cloud bottom, while at the top there is a strong positive charge. Lightning can streak between the positive and negative portions of the same cloud, between two clouds, or between a cloud and the earth.

Lightning is not a single stroke or spark. It is, in fact, many sparks. Three things have happened by the time you see the flash you call lightning. The first, which takes about one-mil-

LIFE CYCLE OF A LIGHTNING STROKE

As thunderstorm induces growing positive charge in earth, potential between cloud and ground increases (1) until pilot leader starts a conductive channel toward ground (2) followed by step leaders, (3) which move downward for short intervals (4) until met by streamers from ground. Return stroke from ground illuminates branches (5) and seems to come from cloud. Main stroke is followed by sequence of dart leaders and returns (6, 7) until potential is reduced or ionized path is dispersed (8). Elapsed time: about one second.

lionth of a second, is that a leader stroke blazes a path, or trail, for the lightning bolt that follows. Next, for no longer than 200 millionths of a second, a surge of high-voltage electricity races back up the blazed trail from the contact point. Remember, the contact point may be in the same cloud, on another cloud, or at some point on the earth. The third thing that happens you actually witness, that is, the lightning flash. The lightning flash you see is a sustained current which may endure for as long as one-tenth of a second. It moves between the negative portion of the cloud and the contact point, or point of discharge.

A lightning stroke moving between a cloud and the earth has an interesting life cycle. Normally, the earth is negatively charged with respect to the atmosphere. But when a thunderhead passes over a portion of the earth, the negative charge in the base of the cloud induces an opposite charge on the ground. Thus, the ground immediately below the cumulonimbus cloud develops a positive charge. This positive charge may, in fact, exist for several miles around the storm. If the storm is moving

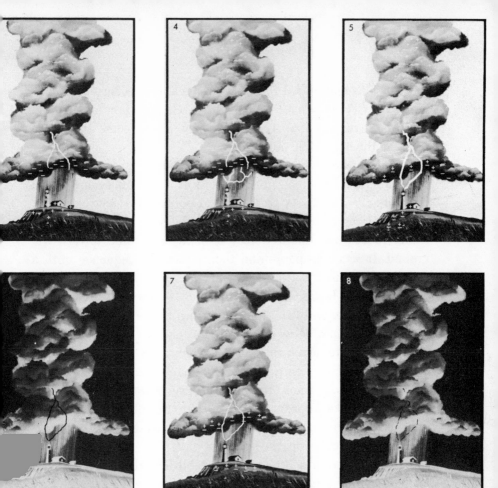

at twenty miles an hour, the ground charge follows the cloud like an electrical shadow.

As the thunderhead matures, the negative charge in its base grows stronger. This, in turn, induces the positively-charged electrical shadow following the cloud to become stronger. Finally, the attraction between the positive charges in the ground and the negative charges in the cloud causes the positive ground current to flow up buildings, trees, and other elevated objects. The charges seem to be attempting to establish contact with each other.

Air is a poor conductor of electricity. It tends to insulate the negative charges in the cloud from the positive charges in the ground. This means that the air prevents a flow of current. Lightning occurs only after huge electrical charges accumulate and their push, or potential, is great enough to overcome the resistance of the insulating air.

The typical cloud-to-ground stroke begins as a pilot leader. The leader stroke is too faint to be visible. It advances downward from the cloud and sets up the initial portion of the stroke path. A surge of current called a *step leader* follows the pilot. The step leader moves one hundred feet or more at a time toward the ground. It seems to pause and then repeat the sequence until a path of electrified particles is near the ground.

When the leader stroke approaches the ground, a discharge streamer is extended from the ground up to the leader and completes the channel between the ground and the cloud. Once the path is complete, a return stroke leaps upward from the ground to the cloud. This return stroke illuminates the branches of the descending leader track. Because the leader tracks point downward, the stroke appears to come from the cloud. The bright light of the return stroke is produced by glowing atoms and molecules which make up the air.

After the return stroke has established the channel, dart leaders from the cloud initiate secondary returns. A secondary return is a rush of electrical energy from the cloud down to the earth. These secondary returns continue until the opposing charges are dissipated or the channel is, in fact, disrupted by air movements.

Thunder has its origin in the explosion that occurs along the path of the lightning channel. When the discharge occurs, a flood of electrons hits the air along the channel with sudden violence. This causes intense heating—often to temperatures of 18,000° F —and produces an abrupt expansion of the air particles. The air expands in all directions creating a compression or booming sound wave in the surrounding atmosphere.

The "roll" of thunder can be explained as a time-lapse phenomenon. Lightning follows a zigzag path along the channel.

The sound waves created by the expanding air along the channel start out simultaneously. Each compression wave reaching your ear has traveled a different distance. Since they do not all arrive simultaneously, you hear a roll, or rumble. A prolonged roll is the result of multiple discharges in quick succession. The rumble of thunder may also be accentuated by the presence of mountains, hills, and valleys. These obstructions are really sound-reflecting surfaces. Clouds and buildings also can reflect the sound to produce the rumbling that we often hear.

Light travels with a speed of 186,000 miles per second. Sound, on the other hand, travels through air at roughly 767 miles per hour. The speed of light is about one million times that of sound. If you hear the roll of thunder, you can estimate the distance to the lightning discharge. Count the number of seconds between the time you see the lightning and the time you hear the thunder and then divide by five. In other words, if you see a flash of lightning and then hear the roll of thunder ten seconds later, the distance from where you are standing to the lightning stroke is approximately two miles.

Lightning appears to come in many forms: forked, streak, zigzag (or chain), sheet, heat, and ball. But all lightning strokes are basically the same. The appearance of different forms depends upon the position of the observer. Forked, streak, zigzag or chain lightning is observed when you are within a few miles of the discharge and the winding path is within clear, unobstructed view.

Sheet lightning appears to have no particular form. It is observed as a bright flash that spreads all over the horizon and lights up the sky. Sheet lightning is the light from a regular discharge. It is really forked, zigzag or chain lightning, but it occurs beyond your horizon. Therefore, you cannot observe it directly.

Heat lightning is usually observed on a summer evening and produces a similar effect to sheet lightning. The flashes, however, are fainter; and thunder usually does not accompany them.

Again, the effect called *heat lightning* is simply too far away for the thunder to be heard. It is way beyond the observer's horizon.

Ball lightning is a peculiar, often spectacular, kind of electrical discharge. It appears as a round or elliptical moving blot of light. At times it appears to be four inches in diameter, sometimes larger. At other times, it may seem to be as small as a walnut. People have described these balls as being colored red, yellow, white, or even blue. The balls appear during a regular lightning storm. They have been observed to decay, or dwindle away, slowly on some occasions. Other observers have noted that balls disappear with a sharp explosive pop.

There is a great deal of controversy with respect to just how ball lightning is formed. Some scientists suggest that the balls originate at the point of contact between a downward leader from a cloud and a streamer rising from the ground. Other scientists suggest that a hissing globe of ball lightning is born when a lightning stroke springs a leak or changes direction. The change in direction, according to this theory, punches a hole in the magnetic field. This hole allows the escape of an electrically-charged jet of hot gas under high pressure. As the escaping, expanding gas flows across the magnetic field, it is rolled into a ball.

Because tall objects attract lightning, it is wise to install well-grounded lightning rods atop large buildings. One of the very favorite targets of lightning in the United States is the Empire State Building. It is regularly struck, often as many as seventy times a year. In fact, it was once struck fifteen times in fifteen minutes during a violent thunderstorm. But it is a very safe building because the electrical discharge follows the steel until it is safely grounded.

Lightning strokes come in at least two sizes. Evidence to support this contention was gathered when lightning struck two television towers atop Mt. Bigelow at Tucson, Arizona, in July, 1963. Two classes of holes were observed in the metal of the tower. One was ten times the size of the other. Scientists viewing the damage inferred that there are at least two sizes of lightning flashes: one about one-tenth of an inch in diameter and the other about one inch in diameter.

There is one way in which lightning serves man. Lightning streaking through the sky frees the nitrogen in the air. In other words, lightning performs a job of nitrogen fixation just as high-voltage electricity does in a commercial nitrogen-fixation factory. This gift of nitrogen to plant life falls with the raindrops. About 100 million tons of fixed nitrogen is spread over the earth each year as a result of lightning. The nitrogen added to the soil in this way enriches plant growth.

But, in all other instances, lightning is dangerous because it carries high currents and produces destructive heating effects. Lightning can cause damage to aircraft, and it can also disrupt communications and navigation equipment. Persons struck by lightning receive severe electric shocks and sometimes burns. Proper first aid, that is, artificial respiration, can sometimes revive lightning victims. Once the person has been struck by lightning, he carries no electrical charge and he can be handled safely.

Lightning has been the cause of many disasters. On June 22, 1918, for example, lightning struck a flock of sheep in the Wasatch National Forest of Utah. The sheep were bunched together in an open field and one stroke of lightning killed 500 of them. Then on July 10, 1926, the Navy's largest ammunition depot, situated at Lake Denmark, New Jersey, was blown sky-high. A bolt of lightning struck a small building and set off depth charges and TNT bombs stored within the building. This explosion occurred even though the building was protected by lightning rods. Sixteen people were killed. Property worth seventy million dollars was destroyed and all the buildings for one-half mile around were damaged with debris scattered for more than twenty miles.

Environmental Science Services Administration has developed fifteen safety rules which will help you save your life when lightning threatens. It is a good idea to review these rules and to

MEN AND MACHINES ARE NEEDED TO FIGHT FOREST FIRES

act upon them in the event that you are in an area threatened by severe thunderstorms:

Stay indoors, and don't venture outside, unless absolutely necessary.

Stay away from open doors and windows, fireplaces, radiators, stoves, metal pipes, sinks, and plug-in electrical appliances.

Don't use the telephone during the storm—lightning may strike telephone lines outside.

Don't use plug-in electrical equipment like hair dryers, electric tooth brushes, or electric razors during the storm.

Don't take laundry off the clothesline.

Don't work on fences, telephone or power lines, pipelines, or structural steel fabrication.

Don't use metal objects like fishing rods and golf clubs. Golfers wearing cleated shoes make good lightning rods.

Don't handle flammable materials in open containers.

Stop tractor work, especially when the tractor is pulling metal equipment, and dismount. Tractors and other implements in metallic contact with the ground are often struck by lightning.

Get out of the water and off small boats.

Stay in your automobile if you are traveling. Automobiles offer excellent lightning protection.

Seek shelter in buildings. If no buildings are available, your best protection is a cave, ditch, canyon, or under head-high clumps of trees in open forest glades.

When there is no shelter, avoid the highest object in the area. If only isolated trees are nearby, your best protection is to crouch in the open, keeping twice as far away from isolated trees as the trees are high.

Avoid hill tops, open spaces, wire fences, metal clotheslines, exposed sheds, and any electrically conductive elevated objects.

When you feel the electrical charge—if your hair stands on end or your skin tingles—lightning may be about to strike you. Drop to the ground immediately.

5. Terrifying Twisters

A funnel-shaped cloud spins toward the earth.

5. Terrifying Twisters

At least eight tornadoes clawed through farms, forests, and lakeside resorts in northern Minnesota on August 5, 1969. The tornadoes swooped out of a twilight sky and caught vacationers on beaches and in flimsy resort cabins. Twelve persons were killed and hundreds were injured.

The twisters that struck Minnesota were spawned in black thunderclouds that followed a day of stifling heat and high humidity. One observer said the storm hit with a "pure white curtain of wind-driven rain." Buildings were flattened, trees uprooted, gasoline pumps wrenched from their concrete foundations, and utility poles were toppled.

A visitor to the area described the scene as the worst destruction he had ever seen. Trees were whiplashed in every direction, shattered and piled like twisted wooden matches. In fact, so many fallen trees blocked roads and highways that rescuers had to cut their way through with chain saws and then plow the debris aside with bulldozers.

Of all the winds that sweep across our earth, tornadoes are the most violent. There is currently no way to alter the path or reduce the violence of these storms. Fortunately, the time during which a tornado is in contact with the earth is rather brief; and its destructive path is usually short. The average tornado, for example, maintains contact with the earth for a distance of only sixteen miles. During this time, it travels from 25 to 40 miles an hour.

The tornado itself is characterized by a spinning funnel-shaped cloud. The color of the cloud ranges from black to gray. The average width of the path it cuts as it brushes the earth is between 300 and 400 yards.

The wind speeds within a tornado have never been measured directly by instruments exposed in the funnel. Obviously, any instrument in its path is invariably destroyed. Estimates of the wind speed, however, have been made by careful studies of tornado damage. The whirling winds of some tornadoes may be as high as 500 miles per hour.

Vivid evidence of the narrowness of the path of a twister and of the force of its winds is shown in the photograph of the remains of a 700-foot Gulf Coast television tower. This tower stood just west of the Isle of Capri Road in Collier County, Florida. The television tower was instantaneously floored when churning winds ripped it apart. It was built to withstand the onslaught of high winds, but the tower was no match for the winds of the tornado that moved across it.

In fact, the twister, spawned by a low-pressure storm area, not only toppled the 700-foot antenna of the Gulf Coast television system, but skipped across the land in a touch-and-go fashion and also leveled shelters used by school children waiting for buses and tore the roof from a home. It touched down and leaped skyward and then touched down again in various areas of Naples,

The 700-foot television tower is crumpled and spread before us. The twister dipped down, struck, destroyed the tower, and skipped away leaving everything else around the tower untouched.

Florida. It bounced over the outskirts of a farming community, touched down and tore out power poles, and then plunged a wide area into darkness.

A migrant farm worker driving down a dirt road entrance to a farming camp described the onslaught of the tornado in this way: "The rain suddenly stopped and a black cloud came toward the car. It hit the car and turned it around three or four times in the air, then set it down right side up again. A two-by-four board hit the windshield while it was in the air."

Observers said the tornado dropped to the ground just east of the highway, came down a bank, cut a swath about 30 yards wide and 200 yards long, lifted into the air, and went over the flat farmlands. Then it touched down briefly at the farming camp, but did no damage there. Before and after the tornado hit, there were torrential rains.

LEFT, *high winds are buffeting our car and ripping through the palms. The tornado has dipped down into this area, and we are searching for the damage.*

RIGHT, *we came upon this snapped tree and the roof lying beside it. The twister was here a short time before we arrived. High winds are still blowing, it's quite dark and rain is falling intermittently.*

Wind is blowing and rain is pelting us. It's not easy to take a picture under these conditions. The tornado winds stripped the roof covering and exposed the boards below.

Badcock Furniture Company erected this bus shelter. Tornado winds dipped into the area and the shelter collapsed. The sign behind the shelter was left intact.

The tornado winds lifted the roof from this house: tile covering, boards, and joists. The tree to the side of the garage and the watering pail on the lawn were not disturbed. Heavy rains were still falling when this photograph was taken.

A tornado is a local storm. It is visible as a vortex or a whirlpool structure of winds rotating at very high speeds about a hollow cavity. In the Northern Hemisphere, winds turn counterclockwise. The centrifugal force of the whirling wind produces a vacuum with an extremely low barometric pressure.

The funnel-shaped tornado develops in a low, heavy cumulonimbus cloud. The funnel seems to rise and fall from the cloud as it extends toward the earth. When it forms, the funnel seems to be very fragile and behaves like a thin rope writhing and whipping, first in one direction and then another.

The condensation that occurs around the whirling vortex produces a pale cloud. In fact, initially you see a tornado funnel because of the condensation. The air surrounding the funnel—although part of the tornado—is invisible until the storm moves along the ground and the outer ring of counterclockwise rotating air becomes dark with dust and debris. Eventually, the entire funnel becomes darkened by this debris.

The tornado funnel always develops in association with the lower portion of an exceptionally violent thunderstorm. Heavy rain, or even hail, usually precedes and follows the appearance of a tornado. Whenever the tornado funnel reaches the earth, there is almost total destruction. A deafening roar and semidarkness move with it.

Conditions which breed tornadoes develop when two highly contrasted air masses collide. Maritime tropical (mT) air, for example, moving up from the Gulf of Mexico or from the equatorial region of the Atlantic Ocean, is usually warm and moist. Such an mT air mass has entirely different characteristics from continental polar (cP) air coming out of Canada. The cP air is usually cold and dry by comparison to the mT air. When such contrasting air masses, that is, air differing in temperature, moisture, and wind-flow pattern, collide, tornadoes may spawn.

Most frequently, tornadoes spawn when cold, dry air rides above warm, moist air. When such an override occurs, complicated energy transformations begin. The deadly whirling funnel of the twister grows out of the collision of the two air masses and the energy transfers that take place between them.

The best trigger conditions for tornado formation seem to occur when the warm air is at least 8,000 to 10,000 feet thick. The cold air, on the other hand, does its best to trigger the tornado when its temperature falls rapidly with height and when it also overruns the warm air at a steep angle. These conditions encourage the formation of eddies along the plane of contact. The eddies that form are similar to those that occur in a body of water where two currents of different velocity come together. The vortex of a tornado usually develops from an eddy. Thus the vortex, or tornado, is a by-product of the enormous turbulence and energy transfer produced by the collision of two dissimilar air masses.

There is no place in the world that is more favorable for tornado formation than the relatively flat region lying east of the Rocky Mountains. It is in this central part of the United States that comparatively dry air from the west or northwest frequently overrides moist air masses moving northward from the Gulf of Mexico. Although conditions over the continental plains are very favorable for tornado formation, they can and do occur in other parts of the world and in all fifty states. But we should make it clear that, in Europe, Africa, Asia, Central America, and South America, these storms occur only at irregular intervals. In North America and Australia, on the other hand, these storms occur regularly and with great frequency.

The states of Texas, Oklahoma, Kansas, Nebraska, Missouri, and Florida are, on the average, visited by more than 25 tornadoes each year. Colorado, North Dakota, South Dakota, Minnesota, Wisconsin, Michigan, Illinois, Indiana, Ohio, South Carolina, Georgia, Alabama, Mississippi, Louisiana, and Arkansas experience between 10 and 24 of these storms each year. North Carolina, Tennessee, Kentucky, Pennsylvania, Massachusetts, New Mexico, and Wyoming have a yearly average of 5 to 9 tornadoes, while Maine, New Hampshire, Vermont, New York,

Connecticut, New Jersey, Delaware, Maryland, Virginia and West Virginia, Arizona, Utah, Idaho, Montana, Washington, and California expect from 1 to 4. Five states (Alaska, Hawaii, Rhode Island, Nevada, and Oregon) have less than one each year.

Texas, as we all know, is a rather large state. It, on the average, records more than 25 tornadoes per year. In fact, during the period from 1953 through 1970, the average annual frequency of tornadoes in Texas ran around 109. But if we examine the frequency of tornadoes per unit area, we find that the frequency is smaller in Texas than in a state such as Iowa which records between 10 and 24 tornadoes per year. In fact, on the basis of area, Iowa recorded the greatest tornado frequency during a recent thirty-five-year period. On the average of 2.8 tornadoes per year per 10,000 square miles occurred in Iowa. Again on the basis of area, Kansas, Arkansas, Oklahoma, and Mississippi were right behind Iowa.

No season of the year is free of tornadoes, but normally the number is at its lowest in the United States during the winter. December and January are the months with the lowest frequency. Sometime in February, the frequency begins to increase. It continues to build during March and April, reaches a peak in May, then begins to decrease in June. The three months of April, May, and June have the greatest total frequency. In terms of the seasons, it is during the spring months that most tornadoes occur.

Tornadoes may strike at any hour. But the conditions under which they spawn seem to become most favorable during the warmest part of the day. Thus, generally speaking, it is during the afternoon that they are likely to hit. Approximately 82 per cent of all tornadoes occur between noon and midnight. If we examine this span of twelve hours, we find that the hours between 4 and 6 have the greatest concentration. More than 23 per cent of all tornadoes strike within the two-hour span between 4 P.M. and 6 P.M.

From month to month, the center of maximum frequency shifts from one section of the United States to another. In February, for example, when tornado frequency begins to increase, the center of maximum frequency lies over the central Gulf states. But as we move from February into March, the center shifts eastward to the southeast Atlantic states. Tornado frequency reaches a peak in the southeast Atlantic states during April. As spring wears on, the center shifts to the southern plains states; and then, during May, these states are visited by more tornadoes than any other section of the country. In June, the center of frequency moves northward to the northern plains and the Great Lakes. This center covers an area as far east as western New York State.

This drift of the center of maximum frequency is related to the increasing penetration of warm, moist air, while contrasting cool, dry air still surges in from the north and northwest. Remember, tornadoes are spawned with greatest frequency where these air masses collide. The Gulf states, for example, are overrun and almost completely occupied by warm air systems after May. There is no cold air intrusion into the Gulf area to speak of after May. This is also substantially the case across the nation after June. Thus, the center of frequency shifts with the changing pattern of warm, moist air intrusion into the country.

There is a decline in the total frequency of tornadoes when the country is essentially occupied by warm air systems from June on. Then as winter cooling sets in, fewer and fewer encounters between warm and overriding cold systems occur as the warm air retreats and cold air systems move in and take over the country. Tornado frequency is at its lowest level by December as a result of the air mass change of guard.

The chance that a specific location will be struck by a tornado in any one year is quite small. Remember that Iowa, with the greatest tornado frequency per unit area, averages less than three tornadoes per year per 10,000 square miles. The probability is that a given point in even a high-frequency area will only be struck once in 250 years. This, of course, is what mathematical chance indicates. There are many, many exceptions, however. Oklahoma City, for example, has been struck by tornadoes at least twenty-six times in this century. Then there is Baldwyn, Mississippi, which was struck twice by tornadoes during a twenty-five-minute period on March 16, 1942. On May 4, 1922, Austin, Texas, was visited by two tornadoes in rapid succession. Codell, Kansas, was struck three years in a row—in 1916, 1917, and 1918. And each year the tornado struck on May 20!

The destructive effect of a tornado is the result of three damaging forces: the high winds, an expansive effect within buildings, and the lifting effect of the violent updraft. The pressure, for example, exerted against a vertical wall by the wind of a tornado ranges from 160 to 200 pounds per square foot. There are not many buildings that can withstand such pressure. This tremendous force accounts for most of the trees that are blown down.

The expansive effect produced in a building is caused by the low pressures within the vortex of the tornado. When a tornado moves over a building, there is a sudden reduction of pressure on the outside. The atmospheric pressure may drop as much as five inches when a tornado strikes. Under such conditions, an excess pressure exists within the building. Visualize the situation in your mind's eye: high winds and torrential rains are striking an area. The occupants of the building close every window and every door. From high in the sky a tornado funnel dips toward the building. Within moments, the pressure surrounding the building drops from 29.5 inches of mercury to 24.5 inches. Instantly, the pressures become unbalanced. The air within the building is at a higher pressure than the air outside. A net excess pressure within ranges around 400 pounds per square foot. In such a case, the building will literally explode unless it is constructed to withstand these internal pressures.

The lifting effect of the violent updraft is produced by the strong rotary winds. A heavy object can be lifted by a tornado

STAGE 1

STAGE 2

Tornado.
Madison, Wisconsin.
July 23, 1944.

STAGE 3

and carried a considerable distance before being dropped. Objects such as cranes and railroads cars have been lifted and hurled through the air. Kansas steers have been carried through the air as though they were gigantic birds. And in one of the most destructive tornadoes on record which, incidentally, occurred in a so-called off season, during the month of September, B-36 bombers at Carswell Air Force Base in Texas were hurled through the air and crumpled like so many toys. In a matter of minutes, 48 million dollars' worth of damage was done mainly to the heavy bombers. More than 106 of them were put out of action.

A tornado that develops over the sea is referred to as a *waterspout*. The funnel-shaped cloud of the waterspout, just as in all tornadoes, develops from unstable atmospheric conditions associated with a thunderstorm. When the funnel reaches the surface of the sea, it develops into a waterspout. Because of the lowered pressure within its vortex, air, water, and sea spray are sucked into the spiral. Condensation within the whirling funnel produces a dark inner core of water particles.

In a waterspout, there is a mixture of sea-water particles along with condensed fresh-water particles derived from the air. In many cases, waterspouts produce a salt-water rain shower. Such was the case off Martha's Vineyard on August 19, 1896. The residents of the island were deluged by a salt-water downpour. Salt water had been carried in great quantities up an approximately 3,000-foot spiral and distributed throughout the parent cloud. Visualize for yourself the tornado vortex dipping down into the Atlantic Ocean, lifting up a huge quantity of sea water, and then three hours later dropping it over Martha's Vineyard as a salt-water rain shower.

Occasionally, you hear stories about rains of fishes and frogs. These "fish stories" come from many parts of the world. One comes from New Zealand. On July 13, 1949, the township of Hastings reported that during a brief rainstorm thousands of fish averaging four inches in length fell on a ten-acre field. It is more than likely that the fish were plucked from the sea by a

A waterspout is off the port bow of the U.S.S. F. D. Roosevelt.

waterspout, carried aloft into the parent cloud, and then later dropped along with rain on the land.

Waterspouts are observed frequently off the east coast of the United States and also in the Gulf of Mexico. They are also observed off the coast of China and Japan. In each of these regions, cold, continental air extends over warm water. Thus the conditions are right for cold, dry air to overrun warm, moist air and produce eddies that become the whirling vortex of a tornado.

There is, however, another type of storm that is called a waterspout, but has a different origin. This second type of waterspout forms in a cloudless sky, generally in tropical waters. It appears first at water level and grows upward. At the base of these waterspouts there is usually a cone of water surrounded by a frosting of foam. These waterspouts tend to be small in diameter, and they are not affected by the earth's rotation. Thus, they may turn either in a clockwise or counterclockwise direction.

The surface of tropical waters is subjected to intense sunlight. The energy absorbed at the surface can cause a strong convection system to develop and form a waterspout. But, in any event, the surface layer of air in contact with the tropical water is usually very moist and hence lighter than the drier air above it. Many meteorologists feel that the convective rising that produces a waterspout is probably caused more by humidity differences than by temperature differences.

The wind velocities in these waterspouts may be very high or very low. Some ships that have passed through spouts in West Indian waters reported scarcely more wind than you would expect to meet in a fog. No two descriptions, however, are identical; but there is pretty general agreement about the cone of solid water that appears at the base. This cone seldom rises more than twenty feet above the level of the sea. Probably the greatest height such a cone could attain would be thirty-five feet.

The favorite place for these waterspouts that start at the surface of the sea is in the Doldrums. The Doldrum area is the equatorial belt of fitful winds and calms. There is also constant convection in this area, and the temperatures at the sea surface are higher than those experienced in more northern or southern latitudes. The humidity of the air close to the sea surface in the Doldrums is quite high.

A spectacular waterspout was reported on the afternoon of June 13, 1952, in the vicinity of St. Petersburg, Florida. It formed near the shore and made a terrific roar as it passed over the shallow water. A wave five feet high rushed ahead of it. As the wave hit the beach, trees, sand, and other material roared skyward. The waterspout, however, for all its initial fury, disappeared in a mist within a few minutes.

Whirlwinds are another type of phenomenon that seems to relate to tornadoes. But, of course, unlike tornadoes, whirlwinds are spawned at ground level and may turn in either direction. The dust-whirls, common in many parts of the world, are observed primarily in desert and semiarid regions. They frequently develop on the deserts in the southwestern part of the United States. Whirlwinds can build enough force under the right conditions to cause a great deal of damage.

On hot days in a desert or a semiarid region, the ground absorbs great quantities of energy from the sun. The surface air in contact with the ground becomes much warmer than the air a few hundred feet above. Thus, small, shallow whirls of upflowing and inflowing air start at the surface. These whirlwinds serve a useful purpose; that is, they mix the air. In this way, they prevent the surface air from getting as hot as it otherwise would. But, of course, the whirlwind can get out of hand and, when it does, this means trouble.

Forecasting tornadoes is an extremely difficult and important task. A quick warning is necessary to save those people who might be in the path of these local storms. The task of prediction is made difficult because the tornado represents a local, violent convection in the atmosphere, which lasts only a short time. But through the work of the Environmental Science Services Administration and the U. S. Weather Bureau, conditions that lead to tornado development can now be reliably identified in advance of the storm. The limits of the area in which possible tornado development may occur can also be determined.

The criteria used in developing the forecast require that a number of conditions occur simultaneously: First, an active cold front separating cold, dry polar air from warm, moist maritime tropical air must be in the vicinity. Simultaneously, in the same vicinity, a strong high-altitude jet of cold air from the west must be crossing a moisture tongue penetrating into the area from the Gulf of Mexico or the Atlantic Ocean. When these conditions exist, the United States Weather Bureau puts out a tornado alert. The tornado alert is released through radio and television. The alert is for a definite area during a specified time.

There is a difference between a tornado watch and a tornado warning. The *watch* tells people to go about their business, but to keep an eye on the sky. They should also listen for the latest weather statement issued by the Weather Bureau. The *watch* also alerts law enforcement, rescue, and medical agencies to the possibility of impending disaster.

A *tornado warning,* on the other hand, tells people of an actual sighting or an indication by radar that tornadoes are moving in a particular direction. The *warning* urges those in the danger path to prepare to take immediate cover for protection against death or injury. The tornado warning also sets law enforcement, rescue, and medical agencies in motion.

The Environmental Science Services Administration recommends the following safety rules be followed when tornadoes threaten your area:

SHELTER—*Seek inside shelter, if possible. If in the open, move away from a tornado's path at a right angle. If there is no time to escape, lie flat in the nearest depression, such as a ditch or ravine.*

IN OFFICE BUILDINGS, *the basement or an interior hallway on a lower floor is safest. Upper stories are unsafe. If there is no* time to descend, a closet or small room with stout walls, or an inside hallway will give some protection against flying debris. Otherwise, under heavy furniture must do.

IN HOMES WITH BASEMENTS, seek refuge near the basement wall in the most sheltered and deepest below ground part of the basement. Additional protection is afforded by taking cover under heavy furniture or a workbench. Other basement possibilities are the smallest room with stout walls, or under a stairway.

IN HOMES WITHOUT BASEMENTS, take cover in the smallest room with stout walls, or under heavy furniture, or a tipped-over upholstered couch or chair in the center part of the house. The first floor is safer than the second (or third). If there is time, open windows partly on the side away from the direction of the storm's approach—but stay away from windows when the storm strikes.

MOBILE HOMES are particularly vulnerable to overturning and destruction during strong winds, and should be abandoned in favor of a preselected shelter, or even a ditch in the open.

FACTORIES, AUDITORIUMS, AND OTHER LARGE BUILDINGS with wide, free-span roofs, should have preselected, marked shelter areas in their basements, smaller rooms, or nearby.

PERSONAL PREPARATIONS should include availability of a battery-operated radio, in case of power loss; knowledge of safety rules and how to tell if a tornado or severe thunderstorm is approaching; and change of family plans in order to remain near shelter during a severe local storm threat.

PARKED CARS are unsafe as shelter during a tornado or severe windstorm; however, as a last resort, if no ravine or ditch is nearby, they may provide some shelter from flying debris to those who crawl under them.

6. Hurricanes
Alias Typhoons

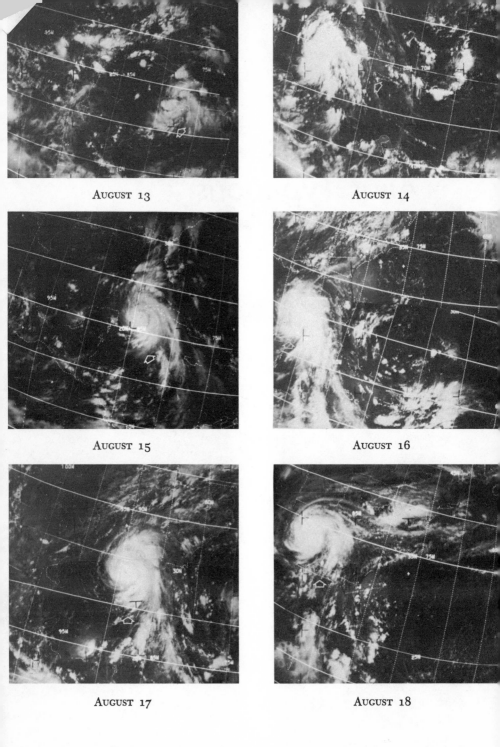

AUGUST 13

AUGUST 14

AUGUST 15

AUGUST 16

AUGUST 17

AUGUST 18

Hurricane Camille was photographed by Environmental Science Services Administration's weather satellite, ESSA 9, as the storm reached hurricane strength in the Caribbean, August 13; passed over Cuba's western tip, August 15; into the Gulf of Mexico, August 16; struck the coastline, August 17; and moved inland, August 18.

6. Hurricanes Alias Typhoons

The United States Weather Bureau issued advisories on Hurricane Camille for days as she churned through the Gulf of Mexico during the early part of August, 1969. Reconnaisance planes were sent into the area. They swooped into the storm and measured winds of 218 miles per hour. Red and black hurricane flags were hoisted aloft from New Orleans across the Mississippi coast and into the Florida Panhandle. The news media received and broadcast the following story on Sunday, August 17, 1969: "Residents of Grand Isle, Louisiana, are evacuating with Hurricane Camille, now aimed at the Louisiana-Mississippi coastline."

All day such news stories poured out. Many people evacuated and left the area of danger. But too many stayed. And some in Gulfport, Mississippi, stayed along exposed areas of the big beach. It was a fatal mistake for these people. Hurricane Camille turned toward the coast and dealt death and destruction to a hundred-mile stretch of the Louisiana, the Mississippi, and the Alabama Gulf Coast. Hurricane Camille spent herself over central Mississippi; and by Tuesday, August 19, 1969, an increasingly grim picture of devastation emerged as receding waters uncovered dozens of bodies and as rescue workers poured through the rubble and wreckage looking for additional dead and injured.

Scores of persons were injured and countless homes and business establishments were flattened as the hurricane moved inland. In the Gulfport-Biloxi area alone, more than two thousand homes were destroyed and an additional two thousand damaged. The entire orange crop in Plaquemines Parish, Louisiana, was wiped out. Hundreds of shrimp boats and other small craft were also destroyed by the storm as well as railroad station buildings and equipment along a thirty-five-mile stretch from Wiggins, Mississippi, to Gulfport.

Pass Christian, Mississippi, was a tranquil Gulf Coast resort community. At mid-August, it was swollen to its peak summer population of six thousand. This community was directly in Hurricane Camille's path. Nearly three thousand people left the town as the hurricane approached. But the remainder of the population stayed behind, seeking out the highest available ground, which was only twenty feet above sea level. The police chief took a squad car along U.S. 90, the beach highway. He stopped at every home to urge people to leave. By nightfall, the winds were blowing at sixty miles an hour and the ocean was creeping over the sea wall. The chief pulled up to the exclusive Richelieu Apartments, which overlooked the beach. Approximately twenty people had gathered on the second floor. They were having a party to occupy themselves until the storm passed over. They refused to leave and there was nothing the officer could do.

A few hours after the officer left the area, a gentle rolling wave as high as a three-story house slammed over the sea wall. It sliced under the brick pillar foundations of large homes. The Richelieu Apartments were overwhelmed by the rushing waters. The ferocious winds tore the building to pieces. The apartments collapsed in a pile of rubble. The twenty persons who had gathered there to party away the storm were killed. For more than four hours, Hurricane Camille blasted Pass Christian with incredible force. Winds of 190 miles per hour ripped everything apart. People were carried off screaming in a fifteen-foot torrent of water. More than 125 persons died in this community.

The scope and thoroughness of the damage defied belief. U.S. 90 is the highway that runs the length of the Gulf Coast from Jacksonville to New Orleans. It was piled five feet high at one point with furniture, boats, and other debris. The damage to the highway was so extensive that it took almost two years to repair it fully.

There is simply no way to defend property against a blow like Camille. But the loss of life is another matter. Many just did not make the effort to leave the area. Others, through ignorance and overconfidence, decided to sit tight and face the storm down. The area had been hit with hurricanes before and many people felt they had ridden out the earlier storms and they could do the same with Camille. It was a foolish gamble. These were the people who were killed.

Hurricane Camille toyed with the people. For nearly two days the storm lurked over the Gulf of Mexico. First it drifted north-northwest; then it changed direction and started to move toward the Florida Panhandle. At one point, it seemed to stop and drift westward. Finally, it built strength and began to move rapidly north toward the Mississippi Gulf Coast. When it made this move, the residents of the area had only twelve hours to make a decision concerning whether they would stay or leave. More than fifty thousand used the time to flee northward toward Hattiesburg and Jackson.

Hurricane Camille destroyed major portions of Route 90. This photo was taken at Biloxi, Mississippi.

Even with timely warning, hurricanes can leave death and destruction behind. This is a portion of Biloxi, Miss., after Hurricane Camille struck.

This is Biloxi, Mississippi, after Hurricane Camille passed through.

These freighters were grounded by Hurricane Camille.

This was the third hurricane of the season and that is why it was named Camille, a feminine name starting with the third letter of the alphabet. As it developed its strength in the Gulf of Mexico, Camille seemed to coil up in a fury before it leaped toward the Louisiana and Mississippi coastline. Three days after it should have played out, Camille stormed north through Mississippi into Tennessee, on into Kentucky, and then turned eastward. It unleashed torrential rains that produced floods and claimed many more lives as it moved from Kentucky eastward into West Virginia and finally into Virginia.

Some two months later, the tropical storm Laurie, meandering in the Gulf of Mexico with winds of ninety miles an hour, was finally designated a hurricane on Tuesday, October 21, 1969. It gathered momentum and began to surge toward the Louisiana coast. The New Orleans Weather Bureau posted a hurricane watch along 75 miles of coastline from Galveston to Apalachicola, Florida. This time, however, the wary residents, now fully aware of the previous hurricanes with names such as Audrey, Hilda, Betsy, Carla, Beulah, and Camille, fled inland.

The cloud formations that make up a hurricane tower ten thousands of feet high and cover several ten thousands of square miles. The winds, clouds, and moisture rotate around a relatively calm central eye like a giant top. Viewed from the vantage point of outer space, these hurricanes seem to be quite small, flat spirals drifting on the sea. But this is an illusion. These eddies in the earth's atmosphere bring death and destruction wherever they encounter man and his civilization. Today we have all learned to respect the hurricane with its powerful winds and torrential rains.

For the residents of the United States, the disturbances that sweep out of the Gulf of Mexico, the Caribbean, and the warm, sunny parts of the Atlantic Ocean are, of course, called *hurricanes*. The name comes from the Spanish word *huracan*. The Spanish developed and derived this name from the Mayan storm god

Hunraken. The Caribbean Indians referred to these storms as "evil spirits and big winds."

These disturbances, however, originate in warm, sunny areas north and south of the equator. Thus, they are found in different oceans, in different hemispheres, and are known by different names. But by whatever name, this disturbance in the atmosphere has the same kind of origin and brings the same kind of destruction with it. In the Philippines, it is called *baguio.* In the Indian Ocean, it is simply referred to as a *cyclone.* The name *typhoon* is given to these storms as they sweep over the Pacific Ocean. In the Pacific, they occur generally from the Philippine Islands to Japan and along the coast of China.

Hurricanes and typhoons start innocently enough. At the beginning, they are mere disturbances of gently whirling winds with a slight lowering of pressure. The rotating earth gives these disturbances their counterclockwise rotation in the Northern Hemisphere and their clockwise rotation in the Southern Hemisphere.

In order to understand the origin and development of these storms, we need to keep a simplified view of the earth's atmosphere in mind: The atmosphere can be thought of as bands of alternately eastward- and westward-flowing currents. These currents of moving air are separated by regions of either high or low pressure. A high-pressure region really means subsiding air. Low pressure used in this way means ascending air.

Over the Atlantic Ocean, for example, a high-pressure system runs from the Jacksonville, Florida, area (approximately 30° N latitude) eastward past Bermuda across the Atlantic Ocean to the Azores and Madeira Islands. This is a region of subsiding air which is generally referred to as the Azores-Bermuda high-pressure system. This system of subsiding air separates a westward-flowing current from an eastward-flowing current.

The westward current is called the *prevailing southwesterlies.* It moves generally northward from the Azores-Bermuda high-pressure system. Remember that a wind is named for the direction from which it comes. When you are north of the Azores-Bermuda high, the winds come from the southwest and, therefore, are called *southwesterlies*. They are, however, moving generally toward the northeast from the Azores-Bermuda high.

The eastward-flowing current is called the *northeast trade winds*. These trade winds move generally from the Azores-Bermuda high-pressure system toward the southwest. When you are located south of the Azores-Bermuda high or generally south of 30° N latitude, these winds come out of the northeast moving toward the southwest. Again note that the name of the wind is derived from the direction from which it comes. Thus, these winds are called *northeast trade winds*.

Below the equator, at around 30° S latitude, there is another zone of high pressure. This high-pressure system in the Southern Hemisphere has a similar relationship to winds over the tropical and temperate south Atlantic as the Azores-Bermuda high-pressure system has in the Northern Hemisphere. In other words, at 30° S latitude, a high-pressure system separates eastward- and westward-flowing currents. The eastwardly current in the Southern Hemisphere is called the *southeast trade winds*. These southeast trades move from 30° S toward the equator.

The easterly trades of both hemispheres move toward the equator; that is, the northeast trade winds in the Northern Hemisphere are moving toward the equator and the southeast trade winds in the Southern Hemisphere are moving toward the equator. In this simplified view of the earth's atmosphere, the trade winds converge and produce a band of low pressure. This low-pressure area is called the *equatorial trough* or *intertropical convergence* (ITC) *zone*. This ITC zone is often labeled the Doldrums on maps and globes.

The ITC zone does not sit over the equator throughout the year. It, in fact, follows the sun. The direct rays of the sun are over the Tropic of Capricorn, or at about 23° S latitude, during the latter part of December. As we move from December to

January, the sun seems to migrate north. By March 21, its direct rays are falling on the equator. The sun continues to move northward so that its direct rays are on the Tropic of Cancer, or at about 23° N latitude, by June 21. The ITC zone follows the sun and moves from its position near the equator in February to its northernmost position near 12° N latitude in August. The day-to-day surface position of the ITC zone varies considerably. Aloft, the ITC zone may occur as far north as 20° N latitude.

On occasion, the ITC zone is so weak that it is undetectable. At other times, the ITC zone is intensely active. The inflow of the easterly trades at these times may produce a low-pressure trough one hundred miles wide with cloud tops rising to 40,000 feet. The weather aloft during a time of intense activity is as violent as that in the squall lines and thunderheads of the Temperate Zone. Under these conditions, intense eddies develop.

When the ITC zone is near the equator, the effect of the earth's rotation is small. But as this zone moves northward, the influence of the rotating earth is great enough to spin a migrating low-pressure system into a tight, violent eddy that may develop into a full-fledged hurricane. The violent eddies intensify to hurricane force, however, only after they pull free of the ITC zone and begin to move north of it.

Once the disturbance pulls free of the ITC zone, it is fed by vast amounts of energy from warm, moist air. It is also nurtured by certain conditions of wind and pressure. The eddy becomes a region into which low-level air from the surrounding area begins to flow. This accelerates the convection already occurring inside the disturbance. Gradually, the vertical circulation becomes increasingly well organized, as vapor in the ascending moist air is condensed. The condensation releases large amounts of heat energy, which drives and intensifies the already counterclockwise whirling wind system.

The inflow of warm, moist air at low levels would soon fill up the system unless a chimney developed. Thus, an important part of hurricane development is the chimney in which converging air surges upward and through which an exhaust mechanism develops. The ascending air moves up the chimney into the high altitudes where it is transported well away from the disturbance before sinking occurs. Thus, the chimney provides a path for large-scale, vertical circulation in which low-level air is spiraled up and away. The air is only returned to low altitudes at some distance from the storm. This pumping action by the chimney and the heat released by the ascending air accounts for the sudden drop of atmospheric pressure at the surface. A steep pressure gradient is produced. It is along this pressure gradient that the winds build and reach hurricane proportions.

A hurricane may seem chaotic, but there is a definite pattern and structure to its violence. There is also a well-defined pattern of winds that accompany every hurricane. In the center of the hurricane, for example, there is an area of relative calm called the *eye*. The winds and rain clouds spiral in toward the eye in enormous bands. Immediately around the eye there is a bank of clouds and the region of strongest winds. It is within this wall of clouds surrounding the eye that the chimney or hot tower of the hurricane is located. The chimney, remember, is the primary energy cell of the storm. Through it, the moist, heated air moves upward from the surface of the ocean.

The winds spiraling in toward the center of the storm bring moist air in bands of precipitation. These rain bands tower to heights of 50,000 feet around the center of the storm. They are awesome sights that extend outward from the storm center for several hundred miles in some of the larger hurricanes. There is an outer perimeter around the whole rotating storm. This outer boundary is usually 300 miles or more from the hurricane center. In the outer perimeter, winds are only moderate and blow in short, flurried gusts.

The eye of a hurricane usually has a diameter of 14 to 25 miles. Typhoons in the Pacific, however, are usually larger than our Atlantic Ocean hurricanes. The distance across the eye of

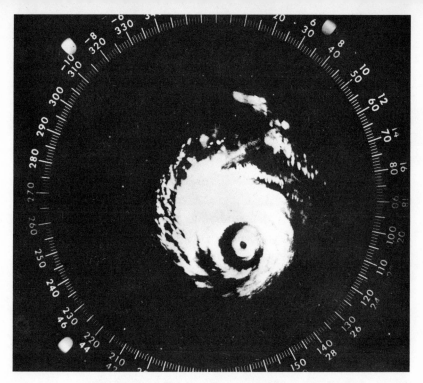

The hurricane's eye shows clearly on radar.

a typhoon may be as much as 50 miles. But whether it is the eye of a hurricane or a typhoon, the skies within are often clear. Sunlight, moonlight, or starlight (depending upon the time of day or night) may stream all the way to the earth's surface through the eye.

When the eye of a hurricane is over you, it is often very deceptive because, after all, you are not safe while the winds and clouds continue raging around the edge. The lowest pressures, the highest temperatures, and the highest relative humidities of the storm are found within the eye.

Atmospheric pressure is generally reported as the height of a column of mercury that can be supported by the weight of the overlying air. In the United States, barometric pressure at sea level seldom falls below 29 inches of mercury. In the tropics, pressure readings are generally close to 30 inches under normal conditions. Pressure measurements made around a hurricane show great variation. At the outer limit of a hurricane, the pressure may be just slightly below 30 inches. As you move in toward the eye, the pressure drops rapidly. Near the center, the pressure may be 28. One of the lowest barometric readings ever recorded is 26.35 inches taken near the center of one storm.

Rain bands were detected only after the development of radar in World War II. Thus, the rain band pattern of hurricanes has not been under study for a very long time. As many as ten rain bands have been identified in large storms. Heavy rain falls from the series of bands, but between them rainfall is relatively light.

Rain bands spiral in toward the center of the storm. They are long and narrow. Rain bands vary in width from 3 miles to more than 20. Their length, however, extends more than 300 miles on the average. The height of the bands varies, too. Some are 20,000 feet high, while others tower skyward to heights of 50,000 feet.

Rain bands indicate the paths of the winds that are bringing in the warm, moist air to feed the storm. As the storm moves, the spiral rain band pattern gradually changes its appearance and structure. A tremendous volume of water can fall from these bands; and, as a result, there is always the danger of potential flooding as the storm moves over land.

There are three general regions of wind circulation within a hurricane: In the outer portion, the winds blow at about 40 miles an hour. The Weather Bureau designates this as a *gale force wind*. Gale force winds can start at distances of 200 to 300 miles from the center of the storm and continue to within approximately 60 miles of the center. The second region of wind circulation begins at this point. Winds blowing at hurricane forces of at least 74 miles per hour are found within this zone. Hurricane-force winds prevail to within 15 miles of the eye. The third region is the zone of maximum wind speed. On the average, wind speeds of 120 miles an hour or more can be expected in this area. The zone of maximum winds surrounds the eye of the storm and speeds of 150 miles per hour with brief gusts of 200 miles per hour cannot be considered unusual.

As you move from the zone of maximum speed, the wind falls off abruptly. Thus, as the eye passes over an area, there is practically no wind. But as the opposite wall of the hurricane approaches, the wind increases again. This time, however, it comes from the opposite direction because of the cyclonic circulation of the storm.

Viewed from the vantage point of outer space, the hurricane looks like a huge top spinning around its axis. As it spins and rotates, it also drifts or walks slowly across the earth. The forward movement of the storm is relatively slow compared to the speed of its rotating winds.

When it is first spawned, a hurricane may move forward at about 10 miles an hour; but in the early stages that follow it may remain stationary while the winds within continue to rotate and generate speed. Then as the hurricane matures, it gathers itself for a forward thrust and gradually begins traveling at about 20 to 30 miles per hour. It moves generally toward the west in a curved path. The curve not only carries it westward, but slightly northward at the same time. But then around 25° N latitude, the hurricane slows and often remains stationary for a while.

The latitude 25° N is sometimes referred to as the *point of recurvature*. At this location the hurricane actually moves from one prevailing wind stream to another. This latitude is approximately the boundary between the tropical easterlies and the middle latitude westerlies. At the point of recurvature, the hurricane gradually picks up speed and then moves forward into the higher latitudes. As it sweeps into the middle latitude westerlies, it may move as fast as 60 miles per hour. But as it moves northward, it also curves back toward the east.

Some hurricanes travel 3,000 miles or more from the time they spawn until they die. The life expectancy of a hurricane

A piece of equipment is being readied so it can be dropped into the eye of the hurricane. Valuable information is gathered by Air Force planes that fly into these storms.

varies. From birth to death for some covers a ten-day period. During that time, it may travel 300 to 400 miles a day.

As a hurricane moves toward higher latitudes, it generally dissipates its energies. The winds gradually fall below 74 miles an hour and the eye fills with clouds or cold polar air. As the hurricane moves into the higher latitudes, it is cut off from its source of moisture and heat and, as a result, the whole storm gradually collapses.

In March, the direct rays of the sun touch the equator and then strike northward. Summer begins in the Northern Hemisphere when the direct rays of the sun reach the Tropic of Cancer. As the sun moves north from the equator to the Tropic of Cancer, the sea and air below grow warmer. The northward shift of the sun also brings the season of tropical cyclones and hurricanes to the Northern Hemisphere. Along the coasts of the United States and of Asia, it is time to look toward the sea and to guard against the storms that spring from it.

Over the Pacific Ocean, the tropical cyclone is never really out of season, but simply varies in intensity. Areas east of the Philippines spawn a number of violent storms and send them reeling toward Asia. The worst period in that region of the Pacific is from June through October. In the Pacific, southwest of Mexico, a few hurricanes occur during the spring and summer; but most of these die at sea or simply strike the Lower California coast as squalls.

Along the Atlantic and Gulf coasts of the United States, the hurricane season is generally from June through November, although May is not too early and December is not too late. The Caribbean Sea and the Gulf of Mexico are the principal spawning areas for these storms early in the season, when the sun is making its sweep over the equator northward toward the Tropic of Cancer. During July and August, however, the spawning center shifts eastward. By September the spawning grounds for hurricanes spread from the Bahamas southeastward to the Lesser Antilles off the coast of South America. At this time of the year, hurricanes also develop in the area from the Lesser Antilles eastward to the Cape Verde Islands off the west coast of Africa. By mid-September, another shift in the spawning area is taking place caused by the fact that the direct rays of the sun are moving back toward the equator and will arrive there by September 22. The principal areas in which hurricanes spawn during late September is back in the western Caribbean and the Gulf of Mexico.

In an average year, about ten tropical cyclones spawn. Six of these usually continue their development and become full-fledged hurricanes. Any disturbance that exists is under constant surveillance by the National Hurricane Center in Miami, Florida. A radar fence that reaches from Miami westward to Texas and northward to New England is used to search for tropical cyclones that may develop into hurricanes.

YR	MO	DY	HR	MIN	SC	TK	ZO	S	ESSA	M	C	LAT	SP	LONG	SP	ORBIT	FR	SUN GLINT,
69	8	17	19	57	28	3	60		9	T	2	35N	5	90W	5	2154	5	31N 95W

This satellite photo shows Camille on August 17 as it was approaching the Gulf coast of Louisiana and Mississippi. Study the latitude and longitude grids. Note the outline of the United States.

This radar picket line gives the Weather Bureau a 200-mile look into offshore disturbances. Cloud photographs from satellites orbiting the earth are also used to spot potential hurricanes. Crews assigned by the United States Navy, Air Force, and Coast Guard use special aircraft to search out these storms and fly in and around them to gather data.

The Environmental Science Services Administration suggests the following guidelines for individual action. These safety rules will help you save your life and the lives of others if your area is threatened by a hurricane:

Enter each hurricane season prepared. Every June through November, recheck your supply of boards, tools, batteries, non-

perishable foods, and the other equipment you will need when a hurricane strikes your town.

When your area is covered by a hurricane watch, continue normal activities, but stay tuned to radio or television for all ESSA Weather Bureau advisories. Remember: a hurricane watch means possible danger within 24 hours; if the danger materializes, a hurricane warning will be issued. Meanwhile, keep alert. Ignore rumors.

When you hear the first tropical cyclone advisory, listen for future messages; this will prepare you for a hurricane emergency well in advance of the issuance of watches and warnings.

WHEN YOUR AREA RECEIVES A HURRICANE WARNING:

Keep calm until the emergency has ended.

Plan your time before the storm arrives and avoid the last-minute hurry which might leave you unprepared or marooned.

Leave low-lying areas that may be swept by high tides or storm waves.

Moor your boat securely before the storm arrives, or evacuate it to a designated safe area. When your boat is moored, leave it, and don't return once the wind and waves are up.

Board up windows or protect them with storm shutters or tape. Danger to small windows is mainly from wind-driven debris. Larger windows may be broken by wind pressure.

Secure outdoor objects that might be uprooted or blown away. Garbage cans, garden tools, toys, signs, porch furniture, and a number of other harmless items become missiles of destruction in hurricane winds. Anchor them or store them inside before the storm strikes.

Store drinking water in clean bathtubs, jugs, bottles, and cooking utensils; your town's water supply may be contaminated by flooding or damaged by hurricane floods.

Keep your car fueled. Service stations may be inoperable for several days after the storm strikes, due to flooding or interrupted electrical power.

Stay at home, if it is sturdy and on high ground. If it is not, move to a designated shelter and stay there until the storm is over.

Remain indoors during the hurricane. Travel is extremely dangerous when winds and tides are whipping through your area.

Monitor the storm's position through ESSA Weather Bureau advisories.

Beware of the eye of the hurricane. If the calm storm center passes directly overhead, there will be a lull in the wind lasting from a few minutes to half an hour or more. Stay in a safe place unless emergency repairs are absolutely necessary. But remember, at the other side of the eye, the winds rise very rapidly to hurricane force, and come from the opposite direction.

WHEN THE HURRICANE HAS PASSED:

Avoid loose or dangling wires, and report them immediately to your power company or the nearest law enforcement officer.

Seek necessary medical care at Red Cross disaster stations or hospitals.

Stay out of disaster areas. Unless you are qualified to help, your presence might hamper first-aid and rescue work.

Drive carefully along debris-filled streets. Roads may be undermined and may collapse under the weight of a car. Slides along cuts are also a hazard.

Report broken sewer or water mains to the water department.

Prevent fires. Lowered water pressure may make firefighting difficult.

Check refrigerated food for spoilage if power has been cut off during the storm.

Remember that hurricanes moving inland can cause severe flooding. Stay away from river banks and streams.

7. Floods: Flash and Otherwise

Aerial view of a typical section of Mississippi River levee. Levees are continuous earthen dams that confine the limits of river overflow. Levees average about 30 feet in height and may be 300 to 400 feet wide at the base, depending upon local soil conditions. Some 1,600 miles of these levees confine the lower Mississippi River proper, and about 600 miles of levees with nearly the same height and width confine the lower portions of its major tributaries and outlets.

7. Floods: Flash and Otherwise

During mid-April, 1969, the town of Crookston, Minnesota, lived through a brutal seventy-hour battering by the rampaging Red Lake River. The river was swollen by the heaviest accumulation of melting snow in history. Rivers throughout the region swelled, and waters gushed over their banks. In five states—North Dakota, South Dakota, Minnesota, Wisconsin, and Iowa—town after town was flooded. In many places, tumbling gigantic chunks of ice were carried by the torrents of water. More than twenty-two thousand people were driven from their homes.

North Dakota was the hardest hit of the five states. Approximately twelve thousand people were evacuated from Minot, North Dakota, when the Souris River went wild. The city of Minot was under six feet of water during the early stages of the disaster. The torrents of water were fed by an ice jam breaking up in Saskatchewan; and, at that time, the Mouse (Souris) River's crest was still a full week away.

At Grand Forks, North Dakota, the Red River surged to its highest mark in seventy-two years. In South Dakota, rampaging waters from the Sioux River struck Sioux Falls. The Army Corps of Engineers said this was the worst flood of the century in the area of St. Paul.

The Mississippi River roared past flood-control walls at more than a million gallons per second or fifteen times the normal rate. The rampaging Red River of the north not only drove water into Fargo, North Dakota, it also drove hordes of rats before it.

During February, 1969, the experts from the Weather Bureau and the Army Corps of Engineers predicted floods in these areas. They based the prediction on the massive Canadian snowpacks that had developed over the winter. Remember, beginning in late December, the direct rays of the sun start marching northward from the Tropic of Capricorn. Spring officially begins on March 21 as the direct rays reach the equator. As the sun continues to move northward toward the Tropic of Cancer, temperatures rise as a result of the relentless heating of the earth by the sun's direct rays. True to the prediction, the Canadian snowpacks began melting with the spring thaw.

In order to protect some of the area, state and federal agencies joined together in an $18 million emergency effort. The Army Corps of Engineers produced 183 linear miles of dikes and assisted 283 communities with their flood preparations. The Army Corps of Engineers also distributed pumps and more than ten million sandbags.

Similar flood warnings were issued by the Weather Bureau in 1965. The 1965 warnings, however, had gone largely unheeded; and the consequences to the communities were drastic. A record $150 million in flood damage occurred during that year.

In 1969 warnings did not go unheeded. Many of the towns that suffered in 1965 were kept dry in 1969 by the hastily built dikes and the other precautions that were taken. But even with all the emergency preparation, damage was extensive. What was kept down was the death toll. Only eight deaths were attributed to the 1969 flood.

Crookston, Minnesota, was better prepared than most towns. This community, with a population of 9,200, had been hit by floods in 1897, 1916, and again in 1950. Experience was a cruel teacher. By 1965, Crookston had almost three miles of new dikes. The dike system had been built by local assessments and general taxes. Thus, when the flood waters struck in 1965, the town was prepared. Even with the preparation, the 1965 flood caused damage amounting to eighty thousand dollars. This was, however, only one-twentieth of the cost of the damage produced by the 1950 flood. Crookston continued to improve its flood-control system after 1965. And it was this improved system that helped the town survive the 1969 disaster.

The people were the important factor in Crookston. Each sector of the community was organized. Dike patrols were set up. Troubleshooting teams and civil defense units were manned by local citizens. Each neighborhood in Crookston paid for its own equipment. Neighborhood headquarters were established and equipped with walkie-talkies so they could communicate directly with dike patrols.

During the 1969 flood, a weak area appeared in a dike built the summer before. It was discovered by a dike patrol. A broadcast for help was sent out by walkie-talkie, and fifty Crookston students responded. These boys and girls worked most of the night sandbagging the sagging dike. Their efforts were successful; and, as a result, more than 350 homes were saved from the rising flood waters.

Long-range planning is needed. Work that is done in great haste does not meet acceptable standards. But we must also recognize that flood disasters will continue to persist as long as

This is the Mississippi River at St. Paul, Minnesota. Industry lines the banks of the river in this city.

local governments permit building on lands that are annually threatened by inundation. And government control is not likely to be imposed overnight because, for more than five thousand years, man's pattern has been to seek out the fertile valleys that surround rivers. For centuries, he has built homes and towns as close to the river as possible. Industry has also followed the same pattern and located along rivers. These locations have been chosen because they provide good access to water transportation, and because the river is a source of water needed by the community and industry.

The encroachment of home, town, and industry on river channels contributes to the damage caused by flooding. Part of the problem in flood control is to halt this movement into the flood plains of rivers. Some sort of flood-plain zoning is needed along most of the rivers of the world.

Recognize that whenever water rises in a natural stream bed above a certain level, floods threaten the area. The danger stage is reached when the stream is bank full. In other words, the channel is completely occupied by water. And periodically, during the history of any stream or river, water overflows its banks. Natural flood plains of rivers vary in width. For example, a river that runs

This is a view looking north at Vicksburg, Mississippi. Notice the flood wall along the city front.

through a steep-sloped valley in mountainous country usually has a very narrow flood plain. On the other hand, a river that runs through flat land more than likely has a flood plain that extends many miles from the river channel.

The torrents of water that overflow the banks of a river carry silt, mud, and nutrients that make most flood plains rich and productive. Fertile valleys, for example, surround the Yangtze and Yellow rivers in China. And because of the fertility of the flood plain, people move back after each disastrous flood to rebuild their homes and to work and till the soil.

Along the Nile River, nature's excess has been put to good use. For centuries, the Nile has overflowed its banks in an orderly and controlled rise. The ancient Egyptians were able to predict the time of flooding. The flood water and nutrients replenished the moisture, kept the fields fertile, and allowed the Egyptians to grow the food necessary for a flourishing civilization. Today, however, modern Egypt has built holding dams and reservoirs so that the power and benefits of the waters of the Nile can be used as needed throughout the year.

Flooding along most of the other rivers of the world is not as orderly as that along the Nile. Serious unpredicted flooding, for example, occurred along the Danube River in 1342, 1402, 1501, and 1830. All of these floods resulted from ice jams during the spring rise. Flood danger is increased along any river when spring rains combine with thawing of major snow accumulations.

Flooding along the Danube in May 1970 inundated nearly one thousand villages and 1.7 million acres of choice farmland. More than 250 deaths were attributed to the rampaging waters, while thousands of persons were left homeless. As the flood waters receded in northern Rumania, the focus shifted in late May to the Danube Delta city of Galati where emergency squads of workers and soldiers fought to keep the water away from factories built in low-lying areas. The 1970 Rumanian floods were the worst to strike the region since Roman times.

Within the continental United States, severe thunderstorms often produce flash floods. A flash flood is a sudden burst of water that pours down mountains, valleys, or desert gulleys. These torrential downpours occur when a cumulonimbus cloud unleashes its store of water in one great dumping operation. The high-intensity thunderstorm of short duration originates in a warm, moist air mass. Most of these air masses develop their physical characteristics over tropical waters such as the Gulf of Mexico, and as a result, are heavily charged with moisture up to altitudes of 8,000 feet. On occasion, the charge of moisture may go up to heights of 16,000 feet.

The moisture reservoir of such an air mass can be tapped in a number of ways. Over level terrain, the load of water can be released by intense heating of the layer of air next to the ground or as a result of its coming into contact with a colder or denser air mass. In a mountainous area, the warm, moist air is usually cooled as a result of being forced up and over a mountain. As

This is a river bed on the island of St. Vincent in the Caribbean. There is not much water flowing through it at the moment. At times, torrents of water come from the mountainous area in the background. During flash floods, huge boulders are driven seaward by the force of the water.

the moisture-heavy air rises, it expands and cools. The cooling leads to condensation. Rainfall in mountainous areas can be quite intense.

A storm in Pennsylvania during July, 1952, for example, spilled thirty inches of rain in less than twelve hours. The rampaging water of a flash flood often washes out bridges and roads. The force of the moving water is sufficient at times to destroy any obstacle in its path.

Flash floods, like the storms that produce them, arrive unexpectedly. As a result, many lives may be lost. A flash flood, for example, that occurred in 1955 in New England dropped fourteen inches of water. The runoff caused the Connecticut River to swell almost immediately. Its waters rose nearly twenty feet and, as a consequence, more than 186 people lost their lives and property estimated at more than two billion dollars was destroyed.

Whenever large quantities of rain are concentrated within a relatively short period, there is a danger of flooding. But a thunderhead is not the only storm that can produce torrential rains over a short span of time. A hurricane, for example, can cause flooding. Hurricane rains in 1955 caused flooding in many streams in southern New England, southeastern New York, southern Pennsylvania, and New Jersey. More than 180 lives were lost and almost $700 million worth of damage was produced by the floods.

Hurricane Camille, in 1969, dropped torrents of rain along the Gulf Coast from Mobile to New Orleans. Camille moved in a sweeping curve toward Virginia. More than ten inches of rain was dropped by this storm on the mountains of Virginia and West Virginia. Massies Mill, Virginia, was destroyed by the rampaging Tye River which was swelled by the downpour. At least 62 people were left dead and 110 were missing as a result of the flash flooding. The excessive rainfall dropped by Camille took everyone in the area completely by surprise.

Over the years, the rains brought by hurricanes have produced tremendous flooding. More than twenty-three inches of rain, for example, was dropped at Taylor, Texas, by a hurricane that swept into the area in 1921. Nearly thirty-nine inches of rain fell in one day and night at Yankeetown, Florida, from the Cedar Key Hurricane of 1950. Hurricane Beulah, in 1967, dropped between twenty and thirty inches of rain over 40,000 square miles of Texas and Mexico. As a result of this rainfall, Mexico suffered its worst flood of this century. Visualize the quantity of water involved when an area this large is covered to a depth of more than two feet!

During the latter part of July, 1969, New Jersey was struck by heavy showers. The rainfall during that period gradually brought most of the rivers to flood stage. On Tuesday, July 29, 1969, the Rahway River overflowed its banks at Cranford. Then the Raritan River overflowed. Stretches of road were under water and causeway bridges in many locations were closed when river waters reached the bridge decks and continued to rise.

Two weeks of almost steady rain fell in New Jersey during July, 1969. The ground in much of the state reached the saturation point. The monthly total at Newark Airport was well over six inches. This was more than two and four-tenths inches above normal. The accumulation of rain in other parts of the state was even heavier. Serious traffic jams and power failures were common.

Stroudsburg, Pennsylvania, with a population of fifteen thousand, is a town close to the western border of New Jersey. On July 28, 1969, it was left with a very limited water supply when the pumping station which supplies water to the reservoirs was inundated by flood waters.

Dams are an ancient but still important means of harnessing rivers. Basically, man builds dams to catch rain and flood waters in times of heavy flow. Then he can open the gates at his discretion to produce power or for the purposes of irrigation during a drought or dry period. Dams are also a form of protection when they hold black rampaging flood waters.

At times, however, man's attempt to harness the mighty rivers and the waters that flow in their channels backfires when an avalanche or an earthquake breaks open a dam, as happened in the Peruvian earthquake of 1970. Unusual quantities of rain or melting snow can also exert tremendous pressures on dams and sometimes cause them to rupture. Whatever the cause of a rupture, such a disaster can unleash thousands of tons of water. If a city or town is in the path of the torrent, a tragedy of monstrous proportions is in the making.

Record rains and melting snows actually caused the failure of three Montana dams in 1964. One of the dams that ruptured was located at Swift Reservoir on Birch Creek. The second was at Chateau Reservoir on Sun River. The third held back water

These snow fields are located above the Rhone Valley in Switzerland. Snow in the mountain areas feeds water to the rivers below. If the feeding is too rapid, there will be trouble below.

in a reservoir at East Glacier, Montana, before it burst. Earth movements at Baldwin Hill, California, in December, 1963, caused an earthen dam to develop a crack. But the most tragic situation of this kind occurred in Italy in October, 1963. The Vaiont Dam gave way, and millions of tons of water spilled over its lip and devastated villages below. An estimated 2,200 Italians were drowned as a result of this tragedy.

A dam is basically a restraining barrier built across a stream or river. The Vaiont Dam was built of concrete as a thin arch dam. The dam was constructed so that it bulged in toward the reservoir in two planes like a U-shaped saucer. Whatever its construction, a dam is designed to hold back a flow of water and to cause a lake to form in the area just behind the restraining barrier. These man-made lakes are used as reservoirs for drinking water, for irrigation of the surrounding countryside, as well as for recreation such as fishing, boating, and swimming.

The pent-up energy of the water held behind a dam can also be put to work. In the seventeenth, eighteenth, and nineteenth centuries, the pent-up energy behind many dams was used to turn a wheel to grind wheat or corn. In modern America, however, the pent-up energy behind a dam is used to turn large turbines to produce electric power.

A dam does not have an unlimited life expectancy. From the moment it is created, there is a slow gathering of material behind it. The streams and rivers deposit soil, pebbles, and rocks in the lake behind the barricade. Gradually, the reservoir area becomes filled with silt and debris. With all their limitations, however, holding dams and their reservoirs are useful in controlling rampaging rivers and in protecting towns and cities farther down the river from the danger of flooding.

Floods, of course, result from conditions other than those produced by thunderstorms, hurricanes, or the rupturing of a dam. High winds, for example, can bring excessive ocean surges into coastal areas. And rivers blocked by large landslides or ice jams can back up over hundreds of square miles. A blocked river is a great hazard because it builds a natural reservoir behind the obstruction which closes its channel. The river water in these situations very quickly spills over its bank and floods the surrounding land. Spring thaws, however, take first prize for causing floods because the warmth of springtime melts the snows on mountain slopes and high plateaus and sends millions of gallons of water on an unrelenting journey to the sea.

The melting of winter snow is the work of wind, rain, sun, vegetation, and soil. The meteorologist knows that certain combinations of these conditions can bring about rapid melting and flooding while others do not. When a warm, moist wind blows across a snow surface, for example, condensation occurs. Each time condensation occurs, there is a simultaneous release of heat. The heat produced in this way raises the temperature of the air and, as a consequence, increases its melting power. Thus, whenever a large mass of fast-moving, warm, moist air moves into a snow field, there is danger. If the melting process which results proceeds quickly enough, it can waterlog the ground and produce serious flooding. This, in fact, is one of the commonest causes of spring floods throughout New England, the Great Lakes, and the Great Plains region. The same combination of

It is important to have gauges on all bodies of water so we can constantly monitor water levels.

conditions produces the spring floods in the mountains of the Northwest.

On the other hand, when a warm, dry wind blows across a snow surface, there is little danger of flooding. Now, it is true that the snow may, in fact, disappear practically overnight under these conditions. But the flooding risk is not as great as in the case of the warm, moist air because warm, dry wind causes a considerable portion of the snow to vaporize directly into the dry atmosphere.

Many people believe that rain causes snow to melt. But rain alone seldom succeeds in melting snow very fast. A rainfall of five inches, for example, with a temperature of 41° F is unlikely to release more than one-third of an inch of snow water. A heavy rain of five inches, on the other hand, occurring in conjunction with warm, windy weather causes the melting rate of the snow to rise sharply. The Red River flood of 1950 was caused by a combination of heavy rainfall and warm, windy weather.

Another popular belief is that the sun is an efficient destroyer of snow. The fact is that the sun has to work very hard indeed to remove any snow when the snow surface is clean. Most of the sun's radiation, under such conditions, is reflected back into the atmosphere. A dirty snow surface, however, is a different story. Each little speck of dirt acts as an absorber of the sun's energy. The energy absorbed by dirt, soot, and other debris on snow contributes to the melting process. In fact, a blackened layer of snow can continue melting even after it has been covered by a new snowfall. Thus, you might say, the sun needs a transformer to change its energy to heat that can be used to melt the snow.

Snow melts much more quickly in open country than in forested country. Trees, even leafless, deciduous trees, cut down on the air movement. Any decrease in the ability of air to circulate in turn depresses the rate at which snow evaporates into the air.

The temperature of soil is a crucial factor in its ability to cause snow to melt. Under some conditions, soil becomes frozen before the first snows of winter fall. Frozen ground hidden below a blanket of snow is not likely to contribute much heat to melt the overlying snow cover.

If soil is not frozen at the time the first snow begins to fall, then the ground below will have a reservoir of stored-up warmth. Once the snow falls, it insulates the ground from the atmosphere. The warmth of the soil below goes to work to melt the underside of the snow. The heat of the soil, under these circumstances, may be sufficient to keep the lower layers of snow in a constant state of liquefaction. Throughout the winter, the slow melting of the underside of the snow blanket adds to the groundwater supply. By the time the spring thaw comes, the risk of flooding through rapid runoff is not very great.

Flood safety rules have been compiled by the Environmental Science Services Administration. During any flood emergency, stay tuned to your radio station. Information from ESSA and civil emergency forces may save your life, especially when you use the following rules as a guide:

Before the flood:

Keep on hand materials like sandbags, plywood, plastic sheeting, and lumber.

Install check valves in building sewer traps to prevent flood water from backing up in sewer drains.

Arrange for auxiliary electrical supplies for hospitals and other operations which are critically affected by power failures.

Keep first aid supplies at hand.

Keep your automobile fueled; if electric power is cut off, filling stations may not be able to operate pumps for several days.

Keep a stock of food which requires little cooking and no refrigeration; electric power may be interrupted.

Keep a portable radio, emergency cooking equipment, lights, and flashlights in working order.

This is the upper St. Croix between Gordon and Dairyland, Wisconsin. During the fall, we usually see a gentle stream flowing through the wetlands. This river, like any other, gets out of hand at times.

This is what happens when water overflows its banks.

When you receive a flood warning:

Store drinking water in clean bathtubs and in various containers. Water service may be interrupted.

If forced to leave your home and time permits, move essential items to safe ground; fill tanks to keep them from floating away; grease immovable machinery.

Move to a safe area before access is cut off by flood water.

During the flood:

Avoid areas subject to sudden flooding.

Do not attempt to cross a flowing stream where water is above your knees.

Do not attempt to drive over a flooded road; you can be stranded, and trapped.

After the flood:

Do not use fresh food that has come in contact with flood waters.

Test drinking water for potability; wells should be pumped out and the water tested before drinking.

Seek necessary medical care at the nearest hospital. Food, clothing, shelter, and first aid are available at Red Cross shelters.

Do not visit disaster areas; your presence might hamper rescue and other emergency operations.

Do not handle live electrical equipment in wet areas; electrical equipment should be checked and dried before returning to service.

Use flashlights, not lanterns or torches, to examine buildings; flammables may be inside.

Report broken utility lines to appropriate authorities.

8. Awesome Slides: Landslides and Avalanches

Gravity is constantly at work trying to move mountain material to the sea. When the task is accomplished with great haste, there is trouble for a town in the path of the slide.

8. Awesome Slides: Landslides and Avalanches

A storm that claimed forty-seven lives in southern California on January 22, 1969, sent a twelve-foot wall of mud ripping through suburban Glendora. The sea of rainwater and mud damaged more than one hundred homes and completely routed residents in the Glencoe Heights section. The mountainous runoff smashed through an eight-foot sandbag barricade at the mouth of Harrow Canyon before cascading into the streets and homes.

Eight days of almost continuous rain propelled the tons of mud and debris down from mountains and foothills. The mud slides hit homes, raced through communities, and isolated entire neighborhoods. At least twelve persons were buried alive.

Reservoirs in Pasadena, San Bernadino, and Beverly Hills filled to overflowing; but the rains continued, inundated southern California, and produced the worst floods in thirty-two years.

Downed trees were everywhere. Washed-out roads were made impassable by heavy debris. Mud slides occurred throughout the Los Angeles area doing extensive damage at Glendora, Brentwood, Bel Air, and the Hollywood Hills. Many homes were filled to the ceiling with the muddy ooze. Other houses simply slipped from their foundations and slid downhill.

Thousands of sandbags were used to try to hold back the muck and debris, but nothing seemed to work. In one two-block area, six thousand sandbags were filled and placed in position, but they were insufficient to restrain a four-foot surge of mud that swept into streets and battered homes.

The terrain in the Los Angeles area consists of flatland as well as hillside. Many homes have been built on the flatland, but it is in these areas that smog accumulates. Thus, the citizens of Los Angeles have naturally looked to the hillsides. Many have taken to the bushy, mesquite-covered slopes of the San Gabriel and the Santa Monica mountains. Spectacular views of the surrounding countryside spread before you from the vantage point of these hillsides.

There is a definite danger to homes perched on hillsides in any location, but it is particularly acute in Los Angeles. On every mountain slope, a component of gravity exerts a pull. When conditions are right, this downward pull of gravity can cause a large-scale migration of soil, broken rock, and even large masses of bedrock. An abrupt landslide results when gravity accomplishes its task of transferring mountain material toward sea level.

The mud slides that caused such devastation in Los Angeles in January, 1969, were the result of a subtropical storm that swept in from Hawaii and hung over southern California for nine days. The storm dumped ten inches of rain on the hills and valleys of the area. The rivers overflowed and the downpour continued. The water began to work on the slopes and the hills, allowing gravity to produce the spectacular slides.

The slopes and hills in the Los Angeles area are periodically stripped of vegetation by summer brush fires. Rainwater falling in torrents saturates the barren ground and separates the soil parti-cles. The water lubricates each grain of soil so that friction is reduced. When friction among the soil particles is reduced suffi-ciently, there is nothing to resist the downward pull of gravity; and, as a result, thousands of tons of soil suddenly slip to the bottom of the slope.

Careless excavation and construction can create and con-tribute to the hazardous conditions that produce landslides. But once the soil is saturated by rainwater and the downward pull of gravity overwhelms the friction that exists within the soil, houses, walls, trees, and just about everything on the surface is carried along with the river of mud.

Rainfall, careless excavation, and faulty construction, how-ever, are not the only causes of landslides. Earthquakes, ocean waves, eroding rivers, and even changes in temperature can also unleash and start tons of earth sliding and slipping down-ward. Sheer neglect and carelessness are two less obvious but important factors in some recent landslide disasters. In the town of Aberfan in south Wales, for example, a huge mountain of black coal-mine waste had been discarded and heaped up during fifty years of excavation. This waste was allowed to accumulate right behind the town. In spite of a warning that the man-made mountain was getting too high, no action was taken to stabilize the debris or to discontinue the dumping. Torrential rains satu-rated the waste and the friction among the individual particles was sufficiently decreased so that 500,000 tons of it was sent slid-ing and spilling into the mining town in 1966. More than 144 people were killed; 116 of the dead were children trapped within a schoolhouse that was in the path of the slide.

In the United States, research on landslides is conducted under the auspices of the Geological Survey. Information from studies is made available to local officials. At present, it is the responsibility of appointed or elected officials in each com-munity to formulate zoning laws that prevent the improper use of land. Most of the people serving on zoning boards are not experts in geology. Very few of them attempt to develop the expertise necessary to make the kinds of decisions that prohibit land from being used in a way that increases the probability of a landslide occurring.

No formal forecasting or landslide-warning program is in effect in the United States or, for that matter, in any section of the world. The lack of a warning system is all too apparent when you read about the tragedies that occur. Tons of gravel and mud, for example, slid down on slum hovels in Salvador, Brazil, on June 17, 1968. More than twenty persons were killed. There was no warning issued to these people about the possibility of a slide.

In most disasters, it is always a combination of circumstances that lead to the tragedy. Heavy rains falling for days, for example, saturated the soil on the mountain slopes in Honshu, Japan. The weather cleared and the casual observer had no way of knowing that landslide conditions were developing within the soil on the slopes. Gradually over the days that followed the downpour, friction among the soil particles decreased. Tons of soil and rock were being pulled and worked on by the downward force of gravity. On August 18, 1969, at the precise moment that gravity won the struggle, two sight-seeing buses filled with more than one hundred women and children happened along. The soil and rock pulled loose with a roar, caught the buses, and carried them into the flooded river waters.

Since the early 1960s, landslides have become a problem in and around Washington, D.C. The Atlantic Coastal Plain in which Washington lies has subterranean clay in many locations. The surface layers, on the other hand, in most of the area consist of sand and gravel. When water filters through the surface layers and gets into the subterranean clay, difficulties can develop. Water saturation of the clay causes "slip layers" to develop in the ground.

Heavy construction in Washington and the surrounding area causes geological disturbances which can undermine or jar slopes.

When this happens in a formation that has a saturated layer of clay, a slide can occur because friction among the particles in this clay is practically nonexistent. The jarring causes the subterranean clay layer to slip and to carry the overlying material with it. Buildings, highways, and other property are damaged when slides of this type occur.

Adequate geological surveys need to be made in all parts of the country. Every community needs to have very precise data on the composition of the soil layers within its boundaries. In addition, there should be a clear understanding of how water saturates the ground. Then long-range research studies should be undertaken to develop information that can be used to determine when critical levels of saturation are reached. The data gathered should pinpoint when slip layers are likely to develop, either at the surface or in subterranean areas. Heavy construction should, of course, always be preceded by careful geological surveys. When dangers are noted, adequate safeguards should be built into the construction sites so that the risk of landslides is minimized.

The Vaiont Dam tragedy that occurred in Italy during 1963 was a case of sheer ignorance and negligence. The Italian government investigated the tragedy for more than five years and then brought eight men to trial in November, 1968. The dam, not far from the international winter resort of Cortina d'Ampezzo, was built despite the fact that the unstable nature of the mountain beyond it was well known.

Surveys showed that there was a clear, evident danger of landslides. In fact, the mountain itself was called *Toc* which, in Italian slang, means "chunk" or "piece." Thus, even the name of the mountain alluded to the tendency of fragments to fall from it. Despite all the information available, an 873-foot-high dam was built. The devastating rush of water over the Vaiont Dam in 1963 that drowned an estimated 2,200 people did not occur as a result of a failure in the basic construction. The tragedy occurred because a landslide dumped tons of debris into the reservoir and destroyed the retaining walls.

Many factors contribute to the development of a landslide. Differences in underlying strata, such as exist in the Atlantic Coastal Plain, are, of course, crucial. The danger in the area around Washington, for example, results from the fact that water flowing through the sand and the gravel at the surface can reach an underlying clay area. Other combinations of rock structure can be just as dangerous and each situation needs to be analyzed. A second crucial factor is the angle of a slope. The steeper the angle, the more danger there is that the pull of gravity can overcome the inherent resistance of the soil to the downward movement. The amount of rainwater that falls in an area is a third factor to be considered in landslide formation. Rainwater percolating through rock and soil tends to decrease the internal friction among the particles that make up a slope. A fourth factor to be considered is the extent of undercutting at the base of the slope. Undercutting removes the natural stability that exists and makes the possibility of a slide more likely.

Every year large numbers of slides occur in mountainous regions such as the Alps, the Himalayas, and the Rocky Mountains. The slides of soil and rock material in a mountain range can vary in volume from a few cubic yards to more than a cubic mile. A large slide that starts without any warning can move at high speeds and overwhelm a town or any obstacle in its path.

It is not uncommon for a sliding mass of rock or soil to block a large stream. The pool or body of water that develops behind the dam produced by the landslide is called a *lake*. When lakes are formed in this way, changes in the topography and the erosional scheme of the area are brought about.

The landslide that makes headlines is the catastrophic kind, that is, the sudden loosening of material that moves at great speed, overwhelms everything in its path, and causes death and destruction. There are landslides, however, that move slowly and

A village in the French Alps.

intermittently. These mass movements are referred to as *chronic landslides*. An observer is hardly aware that the slide is occurring.

The movement of a chronic landslide occurs in an off-and-on way. The slow, intermittent movement may take place over months and even years. The masses of soil and broken rock in these chronic slides move partly by slow flowage and partly by slipping over the basement rock. During the winter, the chronic landslide may remain stationary because the material that makes up its mass is usually frozen, and thus does not have a tendency to flow and slip. The spring thaw, however, causes the soil and rock material to become saturated with water. The water acts as a kind of lubricant that encourages the soil and rock material to resume its downward movement through flow and sliding.

Certain surface features such as a *hummocky* slope indicate instantly that a slow, downward movement is occurring. Trees also reveal the dynamics below the surface of a slope. If the trees are tilted at various angles and some of them have been uprooted, then there is every reason to believe that there is downward movement. Loose, weathered material covering a slope is another bit of evidence that is just as conclusive of slow, downward movement as the persistent tilting of a pole or other objects set in the ground.

Slow, downward creep is a part of nature's scheme. All such movement is designed to bring loose rock material within the reach of streams. The streams pick up the material and continue its transport to lower ground and finally to the sea. The cutting of deep valleys by streams is a part of this natural process which operates in high mountainous country. Streams in the high country create steep slopes that are especially vulnerable to landslides. Stream erosion, chronic landslides, and catastrophic landslides all cooperate in the wearing down of land masses.

A landslide is a frightening spectacle. The forces of nature seem to coil, spring, and overwhelm everything in their path. Man needs to become more adept at analyzing the conditions that produce landslides. He must make sure that he does not magnify these conditions by his actions and thus hasten the process. Danger develops only when man stands in the way of these natural forces. Man must either learn to avoid these landslide zones or suffer the consequences when nature unleashes them.

Each winter millions of tons of ice and snow slide down mountain slopes in a white fury. A snowslide, or avalanche, is, in some ways, more frightening than a landslide. Fortunately, most of these avalanches occur far from civilization in the remote mountain areas of the United States. Hundreds, perhaps thousands of these avalanches occur. As man opens up the remote areas for skiing and other recreational pursuits, more of these avalanches are likely to be witnessed. Some avalanches are likely to produce tragedy if they smash into a village or shear away a forest, suffocating people and animals and inundating roads, rivers, and railroads.

Val D'Isère is a good example of what happens when man moves into these potential danger areas. This village was a fast-growing ski resort in France. Skiers could make reservations far in advance, and they were always assured that the slopes would be in top condition. Picture-postcard scenery was all around.

This is in the Val D'Isère area in the French Alps.

During the second week of February, 1970, the lovely town of Val D'Isère was transformed into a place of death and horror.

It was early morning. Le Dôme, a majestic mountain standing 7,000 feet high, dominated the skyline. Without warning, some 100,000 cubic yards of snow pulled loose from the mountain, buried the highway, rolled over a cement wall, and smashed into a three-story ski lodge with its full force.

At the time of impact, the mass of snow was traveling at a speed of 120 miles per hour. It hit the building with tremendous force. In a matter of minutes, forty-two people lay dead. Almost all of them were buried under the mountain of snow. The avalanche covered a path that varied from 50 to 100 yards wide. The victims got no warning except the sound of the onrushing snow.

The survivors reported that they had the sensation that a tremendous explosion had occurred. More than 300 feet of snow covered some of the victims. Gale-force winds and near-freezing temperatures caused the snow to harden rapidly. The snow that remained from the avalanche formed a small glacier that entrapped the injured and dying victims in an icy coffin.

Avalanches are common around Val D'Isère. Local authorities attempt to block the blunt force of oncoming avalanches by building reinforced concrete areas. The heavy snow and near-freezing temperatures in southeast France during February, 1970, caused more than the usual number of avalanches to strike. Four additional avalanches hit Val D'Isère within a week.

As in most tragedies, investigations were ordered. One finding indicated that not enough concrete-reinforced barriers had been built. It was charged that the town officials had encouraged businessmen to profit from the lucrative French Alps ski trade by issuing permits to build ski resorts in dangerous areas. Whatever the truth in this situation, the fact remains that tragedy struck in the Val D'Isère area and lives were lost.

Avalanches occur in the steep, high slopes of snow-piled mountain ranges. The Alps, Himalayas, the Rocky Mountains, the Andes, and the Pyrenees are some of the mountain ranges throughout the world in which avalanches occur regularly each year. The masses of snow that break loose and slide down slopes in these areas have crushed hundreds of homes. At times, whole villages have been destroyed; and thousands of lives have been lost over the years. A snow avalanche is one of nature's greatest destructive forces. In terms of its ability to produce disaster, it ranks along with earthquakes, tornadoes, and hurricanes.

This is dangerous country. Man must proceed cautiously.

Many factors, including the quality, quantity, and condition of the snow, contribute to the development of avalanches. The angle of a slope is crucially important. Usually an avalanche will not occur if the angle is less than 25 degrees. But if the slope is greater than 35 degrees, there is great potential danger,

Man takes chances that are sometimes unnecessary.

especially if a foot of new snow piles on top of already-existing snow cover. The amount of wind and stability of the existing snow cover are crucial, too. High winds contribute to getting an avalanche started. The angle of the sun's rays and the absorption of heat energy are two more factors that contribute to unstable conditions in the snow cover on a slope.

Often sliding starts when there is a heavy wind and melting going on at the same time. Initially, the mass of snow begins to move very slowly, but it builds speed rapidly. Within a few minutes, the avalanche can be moving at 100 miles per hour and speeds of more than 225 miles per hour can be expected under certain conditions.

Some avalanches are composed of wet, heavy snow, which causes them to travel close to the ground. A wet snow avalanche is the slowest moving of the avalanches. The weight of the snow can cause it to strike an obstruction with pressures as powerful as 22,000 pounds per square foot.

The Val D'Isère avalanche of February, 1970, was composed of dry, loose, powdery snow. Dry, powdery avalanches usually lift off the ground. At times, the swirling mass of snow travels through the air at heights of several thousand feet. The dry snow avalanche moves at speeds as high as 280 miles an hour. A column of compressed air develops in front of the speeding mass and a vacuum is created in its wake. The compressed air and the vacuum both contribute to the destruction as objects are encountered. The light, dry snow of this type of avalanche is like fine powder. It whirls into the air and it can sift into nostrils and throats, suffocating both people and animals.

A sudden thaw in the weather, an extra few inches of snow, the weight of a skier, vibrations of thunder, a sonic boom from a jet, or a pistol shot are among the many things that may trigger an avalanche. One of the worst avalanches in history killed 3,500 people and 10,000 animals on January 10, 1962. More than three million tons of ice broke free from a thawing glacier on 22,205-foot-high Nevado Huascarán, Peru's highest peak. In less than seven minutes, the wall of ice roared down the valley, swept up trees, boulders, flocks of sheep, and engulfed nine Peruvian villages. The greatest loss of life resulting from an avalanche, however, occurred on September 3, 1916, during World War I. A series of snow avalanches on that date killed 10,000 Austrian and Italian soldiers.

In the United States, the Rockies, the Sierras, the Cascades, and the Alaskan mountain ranges produce vast numbers of avalanches. One of the most disastrous avalanches in the United States occurred at the Wellington train station in the Cascade Range of the state of Washington. Three large locomotives, several coaches, and the train station itself were swept over a ledge into a canyon 150 feet below by an avalanche on March 1, 1910. More than one hundred persons were killed, and the property destroyed was given a value of more than one million dollars.

There are increasing numbers of locations in the United States in which avalanches and man meet. The avalanche problem in the United States has become severe in the last few years because of the search for desirable skiing terrain. Much of the best skiing is on national forest lands in areas in which avalanches are likely to occur. As skiers move into these areas, the Forest Service finds itself in the business of attempting to forecast avalanches in the interest of public safety. To do the job, the Forest Service has had to establish some research projects and procedures to prevent tragedy from occurring.

There is also a danger of ice or summer avalanches in many regions of the United States and other parts of the world. These ice avalanches occur when great masses of ice thaw and detach themselves from high glaciers during warm weather. In any case, whether it is wintertime or summertime, avalanches begin when a mass of snow or ice overcomes the frictional resistance of the sloping surface.

Advances have been made in understanding and controlling avalanches. Many of these snow slides, for example, occur around glacial lakes. Surveillance and control of the lakes by draining or damming them during thaw periods is an effective way to prevent these tragedies. Teams of avalanche hunters in the United States have been particularly effective. They search out and destroy potential avalanches by triggering snow slides with explosives after removing people from the sites. But with all our precautions, we have a long way to go to "beat" the problem. Each year, too many avalanches kill too many people.

9. Heat Waves

A combination of heat and drought is devastating to plants and animals.

9. *Heat Waves*

During most summers, a heat wave strikes some section of the United States. The heat wave of July, 1966, for example, covered much of the eastern and middle parts of the continent. High temperatures and very high humidity prevailed. St. Louis, Missouri, was the hardest hit of any metropolitan area. By the first of July, the maximum temperatures were well into the nineties. The maximum for July 9 was 100° and heading up. On July 10, the temperature for the day exceeded 105° F. The minimum temperature for July 12 was about 83° F, while the maximum hovered close to 105°. There was very little cool air in St. Louis during July, 1966.

The death rate soared as temperatures moved past 100° F. On July 10, for example, 49 deaths were reported in St. Louis. Two of these were diagnosed as heat deaths. But by July 13, over 152 deaths occurred with 73 diagnosed as heat deaths. Age and sex were important factors in the deaths. For the United States, as a whole, almost three-fourths of the 1966 fatalities between the ages of twenty and sixty were male.

During the decade of the 1960s, the year 1963 also produced a hot summer with many deaths attributable to excessive heat. As you may surmise, the 1960s were far from being unique in this regard. The history of the United States is spotted with many hot summers. While the country was still struggling for its independence in 1778, a heat wave scorched the East Coast. Then in 1793, and again in 1798, hot summers parched the land. The summer of 1798 was particularly devastating since a yellow fever epidemic was also taking its toll of life.

In the nineteenth century, the summer of 1825 had the distinction of being quite hot, indeed. Temperatures of 100° F were recorded three times in Boston during July. Five years later, in 1830, another torrid summer swept the country. The summer of 1860 was extremely hot; newspapers of July 9, 1860, described a "hot blast" that produced temperatures of 115° in the Great Plains states.

The twentieth century established its right to be considered as a leading producer of heat waves almost at its beginning. The summer of 1901 set many new records, some of which stood for thirty years. There were, for example, 9,508 deaths caused by heat during that blistering summer of 1901.

The twentieth century hit its stride, however, when it produced a series of heat waves along with the Dust Bowl drought of the 1930s. The summer of 1930 was a scorcher, but 1934 was even more severe! Temperatures rose in June and stayed high from June through the middle of August. Thermometers soared to 100° and higher throughout the Midwest. There was no relief to be had at night either because the temperatures remained above 80° F at their lowest.

Trees died; fires rampaged through forest areas and scorched communities. The summer of 1934 was a difficult time for man

Northwest Texas was hit hard by the dust storms of the 1930s. This farmstead is being struck by a dust storm.

The dust banks are four feet deep in most places.

This is a dry watering hole. Severe drought works a considerable hardship on the animals.

Sand drifting does considerable damage.

and beast. The water level in ponds and lakes dwindled and then disappeared completely, leaving dust and debris in dry, gaping holes. The level of water in the Great Lakes dropped by more than one foot. In the far north, glaciers receded and the land thirsted for water.

More than 1,500 people died during the month of August alone as a result of excessive heat. Dust was everywhere in the summer of 1934. It drifted across the land and covered everything. Gradually the heartland of the United States became one huge dust bowl. Heat, drought, and an economic depression gripped the country. Millions of acres of land were laid waste by the terrible dust storms in the Midwest.

From year to year, things seemed to get worse. By the summer of 1936, record high temperatures of 121° F were recorded in North Dakota and Kansas. South Dakota, Oklahoma, Arkansas, and Texas lived with temperatures of 120°. By July and August of 1936, temperatures were reaching toward 109° F in Indiana, Louisiana, Maryland, Michigan, Minnesota, Nebraska, New Jersey, Pennsylvania, West Virginia, and Wisconsin.

These were cruel, hard years in the United States. People were out of work. A large portion of the population was hungry. Dust swirled across the heartland of the country; and, from 1930 through 1936, heat killed nearly 15,000 people. More than 4,700 of these deaths occurred during the summer of 1936 alone.

The heat wave during the summer of 1936 was caused by warm air flowing from the Gulf of Mexico. For almost two weeks this air pushed out of the Gulf into the Mississippi River Valley. The sky was practically cloudless. The sun beat down on the earth and pounded its energy into the soil, parching and drying it. The earth gave up as much heat as possible to the air, and the hot air swept over the people and the land. The heat wave was broken only when the flow of air from the south began to dwindle. Then cooler air from the north gradually pushed down over the area.

There is a direct relationship between excessive July heat and significant jumps in heat deaths. Even today, with our use of summer air conditioning, this relationship holds. Thus, one of the best ways to detect years in which heat waves have occurred is by examining either the July–August average temperatures or the number of deaths in the excessive-heat category.

If we review the meteorological records for the first half of the 1950s, we find that the summer temperatures were on the hot side. The heat death toll for these same years was also high. Many states had their hottest summer of the decade in 1952. The deaths caused by excessive heat during that year amounted to 1,401. This is the highest toll for the 1950–70 period. The summer of 1954 also produced a record number of deaths. More than 978 people died as a result of excessive heat.

Average temperatures were not too excessive during July, 1955, but we can consider that the July–August period of 1955 represents a heat wave because of the persistent condition of high temperatures and humidity. The period covering the years 1956 through 1960 was particularly bad in the Southwest. In Yuma, Arizona, the daily maximum temperatures during July, 1959, averaged slightly over 109° F. It was a hot, difficult summer in Yuma.

Heat is a form of energy. Energy radiated from the sun is changed to heat, or thermal energy, by the surface of the earth. Thermal energy is the major force that produces and drives all weather phenomena. A heat wave is simply a period of abnormally hot weather.

Usually during a heat wave there is very little wind, and there is not much cloud cover. The sun's rays fall on the surface of the earth and beat a store of energy into it. The lower levels of the atmosphere are, in turn, heated as a result of being in contact with the earth's surface. The combination of conditions drives temperatures up. We associate high temperatures with a feeling of discomfort, especially if there are large quantities of moisture in the air at the same time. The combination of high temperatures and humidity is devastating.

The great subtropical deserts—the Sahara of Africa, the Arabian Desert, the great Australian deserts, and the Thar of India—are among the hottest places on earth. These deserts all occur in low latitudes. The Sahara, the Arabian, and the Thar deserts are north of the equator, close to the Tropic of Cancer. This means that from March through June these lands come increasingly under the direct rays of the sun. On June 21, the sun is directly over the Tropic of Cancer. From June through September, the direct rays of the sun are migrating south toward the equator. Thus, from March through September, these areas receive intense sun rays that deliver huge quantities of energy and drive temperatures up.

In the Thar Desert, at this time of year, there is not enough rain to produce a cooling effect. June and July are the hottest months despite the southwest winds that blow. The average daily temperature in the Thar Desert during July exceeds 90° F. The afternoon readings usually soar to 127°. Temperatures in the Sahara Desert reach 135° F.

Nighttime temperatures on these deserts are another story. The warmth accumulated by the desert soil during the day is radiated directly and rapidly into the atmosphere. The desert soil does not store the energy it receives during the day. Most of the time, temperatures drop rapidly as the sun sets. Thus air temperatures tend to be high during the day and low at night. Temperatures in the Sahara and some of the other deserts drop to just above freezing at night.

There are barren deserts in the higher latitudes north of the Tropic of Cancer. As the sun moves north from March through June, it brings a flood of energy to these regions. The barren desert soil "sops up" the energy more rapidly than the soil of other areas in the same latitude. Thus, the deserts in the higher latitudes tend to become hotter than the grasslands and forests. The deserts in the southwestern United States and

Mexico, for example, are hot spots that absorb great quantities of energy.

Every continent has its semiarid high plains and plateaus. These areas become sources of hot air masses from March through June and on into the summer. The Western Plains is just such an area in the United States. The Deccan Plateau of India and the Great Plains of China are similar to the Great Plains of the United States in this respect.

Hot, dry air does not move in as well-defined a mass as cold air. Cold air is, after all, denser and flows close to the ground. Hot air streams outward and upward and moves in broad currents at times. At other times, it moves in narrow, restricted currents. Hot air, because of its tendency to rise, flows up over colder, denser air masses. In fact, hot air traveling aloft may move for long distances without being felt on the ground.

Remember, the sun moving northward from March through June creates hot regions such as the Mexican Desert and the Great Plains. Hot air expands and rises from these heat sources. Regions of low pressure are formed as a result of hot air expansion. Cooler, heavier air from the surrounding environment blows into the area of low pressure thus created. The inward-flowing, cooler air, in turn, is heated as it moves into the hot spot.

Bursts of dry, hot air, at times, break out of a hot spot. These bursts of escaping hot air move horizontally across the ground as huge air masses that tend to be drawn toward a low-pressure area. Hot, dry air masses break out of the Mexican Desert, for example, and move northward into the desert areas of the southwestern United States. Another instance in which a hot air mass moves in to fill the vacuum of low pressure created by another hot spot occurs when the dry, hot sirocco of the Sahara moves northward in spring across the Mediterranean.

From June through September, the sun moves south toward the equator and then from the equator toward the Tropic of

Capricorn. The sun finally reaches its southernmost point on December 22. This movement produces an interesting effect on the Sahara. In winter, hot air masses from the Sahara move southward. They follow the retreating sun. As a result, warm air masses push south into Liberia in the west and southern Sudan in the east.

Generally speaking, heat waves occur when a high-pressure area stalls over a region. High-pressure air slowly spirals down toward the earth. It moves outward along the ground for thousands of miles, while the sun streams down through a radiant, cloudless sky. Then, usually along the western and southwestern edge of the high-pressure area, hot air comes spiraling in from hot and dry or hot and humid areas.

In the United States, some of the worst heat waves have occurred as a high-pressure area stalls over the Atlantic coastal region. The positioning of a high-pressure area over the Atlantic coast allows warm, moist air from the Gulf of Mexico to flow into the Midwest. It is this flow of Gulf air that sends temperatures rising and causes extreme discomfort, especially when it is laden with moisture.

On occasion, a heat wave develops in the eastern United States when the Bermuda-Azores high-pressure system realigns itself over the Atlantic Ocean. The air within a high-pressure system rotates in a clockwise direction. With the proper positioning, the Bermuda-Azores high can cause warm, dry air to spin in from the arid regions of the United States. The warm, dry air rises from the southwestern deserts and flows north and northeast over the central and eastern part of the nation. When this occurs, a long-lasting heat wave develops over the eastern states.

In the far southwestern section of the United States, most heat waves are born on the desert. The climate of southern California, for example, is usually mild and sea-cooled. But, on occasion, warm air ruptures out of the southwestern deserts and moves into the area. The very hot summers from 1955 through 1961 were the result of the intrusion of desert air into the area.

The worst heat waves in California, however, are produced when a high-pressure system sits over the Nevada desert. Under these circumstances, compression-heated, sand-warmed currents of descending air move southwestward. These blasts of hot, dry air that come through the mountain passes are called *Santa Anas*. When they occur, the Santa Anas move into the Los Angeles basin late in the summer season. The Santa Anas make a September in Los Angeles feel like you are being exposed to a blast furnace. The air is almost too hot and too dry to be breathed. Santa Ana heat waves hit the Los Angeles area in 1939, 1955, and 1963. Fortunately, they only lasted a few days. The temperatures soared well above 100°. Maximum temperatures of 110° F were recorded. At night temperatures dropped, but they remained in the high eighties.

If you examine the situation, you can readily see that there are compelling reasons why the United States usually has hot summers. First of all, the direct rays of the sun are advancing north from March onward. This drives back the polar air that has been moving into the country from the Canadian region. As the polar air is driven back, the land is opened to more intense sunlight. At the same time, masses of warm, moist air begin to move landward from the tropical oceans. These tropical air masses carry large quantities of moisture with them. Then there is dry desert air that pushes out of Mexico and moves north into the southwestern section of the United States. In addition, wind howling down the eastern slopes of the Rocky Mountains moves east into the heartland of the country. The winds that move down the eastern slopes of the Rockies are called *chinooks*. They are hot, drying winds.

Throughout the year, there is a parade of low-pressure and high-pressure centers that move across the country. These lows and highs serve to mix the intruding air masses. Horizontal and vertical mixing distributes heat from a hot air mass to a cooler air mass. Mixing also contributes to the dispersal of moisture among the various air masses.

The highs and lows drift in what amounts to the mid-latitude westerlies over the United States. There westerlies follow a scalloped path around the Northern Hemisphere. The large-scale undulations of these mid-latitude westerlies extend for thousands of miles and are called *planetary waves*. The high-speed core of these waves is the jet stream. The jet stream snakes across the United States at altitudes of six to eight miles.

The kind of weather that settles over an area depends largely on the prevailing position and orientation of the jet stream. From March onward, the sun drives the polar front back into Canada. The jet stream keeps to the cool side of the boundary and shifts northward with the polar front. As the jet stream shifts, it carries the tracks of surface weather disturbances with it. When the polar front and jet stream are oriented so that the eastern segment is farther north into Canada than usual, the stage is set for a midwestern and eastern heat wave. If a persistent high blocks the jet stream so that it cannot move northward, then hot, dry air from the southwestern deserts is drawn into the mid-continent. Although the blocking of the jet stream brings hot weather to the mid-continent, cooler than normal conditions often prevail in New England and the Far Northwest under these conditions.

Whatever the cause, the effect of a heat wave is uncomfortable and, more often than not, dangerous for the human being. The human body works to keep a proper balance of heat. We produce heat internally from the combustion of food and from muscle activity. We also lose heat to the environment that surrounds us, by conduction, convection, and radiation. During periods of great activity, tremendous quantities of heat are generated within our bodies. The body must rid itself of this heat in order to maintain the temperature necessary for survival.

The task of dissipating heat is accomplished when blood vessels dilate, or enlarge, and send more blood circulating to the skin areas. Heat is transferred from the blood through the skin to the air. Another way in which the body rids itself of excess heat is through the process of sweating. There are more than two million sweat glands distributed throughout the skin of an average body. The moisture poured onto the skin surface by the sweat glands evaporates. Evaporation is a cooling process. Thus, as sweat evaporates, the skin is cooled.

If a body is unable to dissipate and transfer heat to the surrounding air, its temperature rises. As body temperature goes up, pulse rate increases and breathing quickens. If too much water has been lost from the blood, it will thicken and the person begins experiencing violent cramps and fits of vomiting. Under the circumstances, the central nervous system becomes affected. Convulsions, paralysis, and comas can set in. If the body temperature continues to rise, death results.

When the human body is exposed to high temperatures and high humidity for prolonged periods of time, heat exhaustion can develop. Under constant exposure to these conditions, the body has great difficulty in ridding itself of excess heat. In order to protect itself, the body attempts to curtail heat production from within. Symptoms of heat exhaustion generally are subnormal body temperature, clammy skin, headache, vomiting, and rapid pulse rate.

In certain situations, the body may lose its ability to perspire, causing body heat to accumulate rapidly. This condition leads to a rapid increase in temperature than can develop into a heat stroke as the body temperature soars toward 110° F. Under these circumstances, the skin is hot and dry and the pulse is fast and irregular. The victim of a heat stroke usually lapses into a coma and is, more often than not, delirious. Convulsions and death usually follow rather quickly.

Normal body temperature for a human is 98.6° F. When a person's temperature begins to move toward 104° F, he is in danger. Normally, we cannot stand internal temperatures of more than 108° for any extended length of time.

A crop of winter wheat was planted. Not enough moisture was present and the crop did not develop. All living things have special requirements for moisture and heat. Too much or too little of either is usually devastating.

High temperatures accompanied by large quantities of moisture in the air are very uncomfortable, because high humidity makes it more difficult for a body to dissipate its internal heat. Under normal circumstances, when skin temperatures rise to about 95° F, the sweat glands pour out a salty fluid. The moisture evaporates from the skin into the surrounding air and removes heat from the body. Air saturated with moisture depresses the rate at which sweat evaporates. Perspiration pouring from the sweat glands does not evaporate fast enough to cool the body when the humidity is extremely high.

A formula based on the relationship between air temperature and relative humidity has been developed to give an index of discomfort. It is called the *temperature-humidity index*. The higher the reading, the more uncomfortable most people are. When a temperature-humidity index of 72 exists, we normally find that about 10 per cent of the people are uncomfortable. On the other hand, more than one-half of a group will be uncomfortable when the temperature-humidity index is 77. At an

179

index of 82, almost all people suffer discomfort. Under those circumstances in which the temperature-humidity index is 90, there is actually physical danger for most people.

The Environmental Science Services Administration suggests that the following safety rules be followed when your section of the country is within the grasp of a heat wave or when you are exposed to excessively high temperatures.

Slow down. Your body can't do its best in high temperatures and humidities, and it might do its worst.

Heed your body's early warnings that heat syndrome is on the way. Reduce your level of activity immediately and get to a cooler environment.

Dress for summer. Lightweight, light-colored clothing reflects heat and sunlight and helps your thermoregulatory system maintain normal body temperature.

Put less fuel on your inner fires. Foods (like proteins) that increase metabolic heat production also increase water loss.

Don't dry out. Heat wave weather can wring you out before you know it. Drink plenty of water while the hot spell lasts.

Stay salty. Unless you're on a salt-restricted diet, take an occasional salt tablet or some salt solution when you've worked a sweat.

Avoid thermal shock. Acclimatize yourself gradually to warm weather. Treat yourself extra gently for those first critical two or three hot days.

Vary your thermal environment. Physical stress increases with exposure time in heat wave weather. Try to get out of the heat for at least a few hours each day. If you can't do this at home, drop in on a cool store, restaurant, or theater—anything to keep your exposure time down.

Don't get too much sun. Sunburn makes the job of heat dissipation much more difficult.

10. Winter Storms

Results of a winter storm.

10. Winter Storms

The apple-cheeked boy stopped digging for a moment. He looked up, pointed his shovel, and said, "This is my snow. You dig over on your side." Having asserted his territorial right to the snowbank, he then turned his attention to finishing the tunnel he had started to dig.

This young boy was enjoying the aftermath of a severe snowstorm that struck the entire eastern seaboard from New England to Virginia on February 9, 1969. The storm dropped fifteen inches of snow on New York City and twenty inches on the suburbs. New York City was virtually paralyzed.

In New York City, at least 43 deaths were the direct result of the storm. Elsewhere in New York State, more than 50 fatalities were blamed on the snowstorm. The storm took its toll of life in other areas too: 64 in New England, 13 in New

Jersey. The death toll alone made this one of the deadliest storms of the century.

An icy shell seemed to grip the Northeast during this second week of February. More than twenty-four hours after the last snowflake fell, abandoned cars still blocked major highways. Kennedy and Newark airports were closed during the storm and only began to reopen on Tuesday, February 11. LaGuardia Airport was the last to open and it only had partial service by February 12. Boston's Logan Airport was also hit hard by the storm.

It took almost a week to dig out in the metropolitan area of New York and New Jersey. In some localities, snow drifted more than six feet deep. For at least three days, rail traffic was completely disrupted. And this was the first time in twenty-one years that the New York and American stock exchanges were closed as the result of a snowstorm. The last time these Exchanges had been shut down by weather was in 1948.

New England barely recovered from the February 9 storm when another ninety-hour snowstorm struck on February 24. Snow fell from the twenty-fourth through the twenty-seventh, leaving a record 25 inches in Boston. In many sections of Maine, a snowfall of 60 inches was recorded. And another forty deaths in the New England area resulted from this new onslaught of nature.

The eastern seaboard was not the only section of the country reporting snowfall. On February 6, 1969, Big Mountain, Montana, reported 98 inches of snow on the ground with an additional 12 inches that had fallen recently. Park City, Utah, recorded 104 inches of snow on the ground. Brighton, Utah, was blanketed by 114 inches. Aspen Mountain, Colorado, reported 78 inches on the ground. Sun Valley, Idaho, indicated that there was a 112-inch snow base with 4 inches of new snow that had fallen recently. Taos, New Mexico, reported 78 inches, while Jackson Hole, Wyoming, measured 109 inches of snow cover.

As late as March 20, 1969, Cle Elum District Forest Rangers in the state of Washington reported the snow area above Cle Elum was higher than usual. The first survey of the spring found over 108 inches of snow in the Fish Lake area. The water content of this snow was more than 35 inches. This report placed the snow level at about a foot more than usual.

Many localities are inaccessible; and so, iron poles are placed in the area to serve as bench markers. The poles are fitted with bright fluorescent orange marks that are visible from the air. Thus, measurements can be made by flying over the area. This technique is used in the Cle Elum section of Washington. The first spring measurements on March 20, 1969, indicated that at Gold Creek Point the snow level was 183 inches. The level at Waptus River was 132 inches.

Recall that in June perpendicular rays of the sun are over the Tropic of Cancer. From June through September, these rays drift south, arriving at the equator by September 22. As we move from the latter part of September to October, the perpendicular rays of the sun leave the Northern Hemisphere completely and drift south. In late December, the direct rays of the sun arrive at the Tropic of Capricorn. Then the cycle repeats itself; and, from December through March, the perpendicular rays drift north toward the equator. Until these direct sun rays return to the Northern Hemisphere in March, polar air rules the northern continental atmosphere.

From September on in the United States, polar air drives out of the north, pushing back the tropical warmth of summer. As we move through the cooling-off period of autumn, winter gradually settles over the land. And with winter comes the seasonal parade of storms that dump snow and freezing rain, and spread ice across the land. These storms paralyze cities, inconvenience travelers, take lives, and destroy property.

Winter storms are generated in much the same way as the thunderstorms of summer. A boundary between two air masses is called a *front*. The winter storm originates in the disturbances that take place along the boundary, or front, between cold-polar and warm-tropical air masses. Each air mass has its own temperature, density, and moisture content. It is at the boundary between the cold air mass and the warm air mass that a perpetual war of instability takes place. The disturbances caused by the exchange of energy—heat and moisture—across the boundary can, under the right circumstances, become intense low-pressure systems. These low-pressure systems churn over thousands of square miles in a great counterclockwise sweep.

On the east coast of the United States, winter storms often form along the Atlantic polar front near the coast of Virginia and the Carolinas and in the general area east of the southern Appalachians. Many people refer to these storms as *nor'easters.* They are, in fact, the notorious Cape Hatteras storms, which develop great intensity as they move up the coast. Usually they drift eastward after making their circuit up the coast. The drift takes them toward Iceland where they finally decay.

On November 11, 1968, the United States Weather Bureau reported a major storm marching up the Atlantic coast. It produced rough surf, above-normal tides, high winds, and a blast of wintery weather. The storm dropped a cold, chilling rain along the coastline, while snow fell inland over the northern and mid-Atlantic states. In the wake of the storm, a reinforcing surge of polar air pushed into the South. Freezes occurred at night deep in Dixie.

At the same time, snow was cutting across northern and central portions of the plains and the Mississippi River Valley. Snowfall was rather heavy. It affected travel and made driving hazardous. In the northern Rockies, storms dropping snow followed by chilling temperatures are a threat from mid-September to mid-May. It is not unusual during the depths of the winter from November to March to have eight separate storms operating across the continent.

Intense winter storms are usually accompanied by cold waves, heavy snow, blizzards, and ice or glaze, or a combination

An ice storm does extensive damage.

of these conditions. Even within a single winter storm, the type of precipitation usually changes several times as the storm passes. All winter storms have one thing in common: They have the ability to paralyze or immobilize a large area. The chilling winds, low temperatures, and precipitation also spread death and destruction. When these storms penetrate into the Deep South, they cause severe hardship as well as tremendous damage to crops.

The winter storms that develop over the Pacific Ocean grow out of disturbances that form along polar fronts off the east coast of Asia. Once the disturbance has formed and developed into a true storm, it travels northeastward toward Alaska. But there are some storms that form along the mid-Pacific polar front and take a more southerly path. These storms can strike the mainland of the United States as far south as southern California.

The storms that spring from disturbances in the Pacific do not ordinarily cross the Rocky Mountains. In the few instances when one of them does, it tends to remain in the area and redevelop before it moves out again. One region in which Pacific storms that manage to cross the Rockies redevelop lies just east of the Colorado Rockies. The storms that redevelop in this location are called *Colorado cyclones*. Another region in which these Pacific storms redevelop is east of the Canadian Rockies. The storms that move out of this area are referred to as *Alberta cyclones*. Both the Colorado and the Alberta cyclones tend to move toward the east. The most frequent paths they follow converge over the Great Lakes.

The Great Lakes region itself is another location that generates severe winter storms. It is also an area in which northward-drifting disturbances that originate over the Gulf of Mexico and the southern plains are redeveloped as full-fledged winter storms. Many of the storms that swoop down from Lake Erie make winter a particularly miserable time for the people who live in the northwest corner of New York State. Some of these winter storms dump huge quantities of snow—as much as three feet a day—on the villages and towns in the area.

The air masses that converge over the Great Lakes normally pick up enormous quantities of water. Thus, the storms that are regrouped, generated, or forged over the lakes leave as icy winter winds laden with moisture. When these storms hit the land, snow pours down in large, fast-falling flakes. The snowfalls over the Lake Erie shoreline, for example, occur as moisture-laden winds hit land. The hills in the region cause a pile-up of the air and, as a result, clouds develop and ice crystals form. The ice crystals fall, collect moisture that is chilled below the freezing point, and grow rapidly into huge snowflakes. Heavy snowflakes fall rapidly and usually land in a narrow belt near the shore.

Buffalo, New York, is located at the eastern edge of Lake Erie. The surface temperature in Buffalo is up to 27° warmer than that of the surrounding area. The industrial activity and the normal routines of its citizens cause Buffalo to be a "heat island." This urban "heat island" sitting in the middle of a cooler rural area is creating some special effects. Pollutants from the air of Buffalo pour into the sky and seed the air masses that move over the city. This artificial seeding of the atmosphere, coupled with the "heat island" effect, is increasing the natural snowfall downwind from the city. Thus, not only do we find that man must live with the natural disasters created by nature; but, in addition, man's own activities in more than a few instances aggravate and compound the disasters.

When the United States Weather Bureau uses the word *snow* without a qualifying word such as *occasional* or *intermittent,* it means that the snowfall will be steady and will continue for several hours without letup. A *heavy snow warning,* on the other hand, means that a fall of four inches or more is expected within a twelve-hour period. If a twenty-four-hour period is being considered, the snowfall must be six inches or more to warrant a heavy snow warning.

Other designations are also used by the Weather Bureau in reporting to the public: *snow flurries, snow squalls, blowing and drifting snow, drifting snow,* and *blizzards.* A meteorologist defines a snow flurry as snow falling for a short duration or at intermittent periods. The accumulation of snow, under these conditions, is generally very small. A snow squall is a brief, intense fall of snow that is comparable to a summer rain shower. Snow squalls are generally accompanied by gusty surface winds. Strong winds and falling snow, or strong winds and loose snow on the ground, usually mean that snow will be lifted from the surface by the wind and blown about so that horizontal visibility is restricted. Under such conditions, a designation of *blowing and drifting snow* is given.

A blizzard is one of the most dramatic of winter storms. It is characterized by low temperatures and by strong winds carrying large amounts of snow. A blizzard warning is issued when winds of 35 miles an hour accompanied by falling snow are expected. The snow that falls is usually in the form of fine powdery particles. The winds cause these snowflakes to be whipped around

The weight of the ice is too much for the tree. It bows to the inevitable, slowly and gracefully.

with such speed and intensity that visibility is often only a few yards. The temperatures in such storms normally hover around 20° F or lower. Low temperatures usually prevail for an extended period of time. A severe blizzard warning is issued when wind speeds of 45 miles per hour and temperatures of 10° F or lower are expected along with great quantities of falling snow.

Very few sections of the United States can consider themselves free and safe from blizzards. In fact, blizzards do not occur exclusively during the winter, but can strike at various times of the year. One of the worst spring blizzards occurred from March 22 through March 25, 1957. Four states—Kansas, Texas, New Mexico, and Oklahoma—were struck by blowing snow that reduced visibility to zero most of the time. Snow drifts of 20–25 feet were common in Kansas. Drifts of more than 30 feet were reported. Such tremendous drifts halted traffic and isolated many communities. There were ten deaths each in Kansas and Texas, with one death in New Mexico. There was a tremendous loss of livestock throughout the area. The damage from this storm exceeded six million dollars.

Most of us associate snow with the northern areas of our country, but snow has been seen in the air as far south as Fort

Myers at 26° 35′ N latitude on the Gulf coast of Florida. This trace of snow occurred on February 13, 1899. At that time, one of the greatest of all modern polar outbreaks occurred, and cold polar air reached deep into the South.

On January 8, 1959, polar air again penetrated deep into the south. Traces of snow were seen in the Tampa-Lakeland-Orlando section of central Florida. In fact, the winter of 1959 proved to be particularly cold in Florida. Tampa, at 27° 48′ N latitude on the west coast of Florida, had only experienced snow on two prior occasions—both during the nineteenth century. Reports indicate that enough snow fell to make snowballs—if you consider a tenth of an inch of snow sufficient to make snowballs.

Savannah, Georgia, is located at approximately 32° N latitude. It is in coastal Georgia and, since 1871, has had only two snows that amounted to anything. On January 18, 1893, a full inch was measured on the ground, and on February 12, 1899, a depth of two inches was recorded. But residents and records of the area indicate that it was different in the "old days." According to newspaper accounts, a gigantic snowfall of eighteen inches fell on Savannah on January 9, 1800. In fact, a Mr. Abiel Holmes, who was serving as a tutor at a plantation twenty-five miles southwest of Savannah, reported eighteen inches of snow with drifts to three feet. Abiel Holmes, the father of Oliver Wendell Holmes, was considered an experienced weather-watcher and therefore a reliable reporter.

Coastal North Carolina seems to be protected from deep snows as a result of the warm influence of the Gulf Stream. Although it is true that Wilmington and Cape Hatteras have had twelve-inch snows, such storms have occurred only once in each location. On December 30, 1917, for example, Cape Hatteras had its first and only recorded twelve-inch snowfall. Once you get around the Cape, however, and go slightly northward, the possibility of deep snow increases rapidly. Just north of Cape Hatteras is the spawning ground for nor'easters where cold air masses and great quantities of moisture meet.

Mountainous regions are, of course, notorious for having extremely heavy snowfalls. Areas in the Himalaya Mountains probably produce the greatest annual snowfall in the world. But even in the Himalayas there is much variety. On the western passes between 17,000 and 19,000 feet, for example, the snowfall is generally not more than three feet. In the Himalaya passes farther east, however, the snowfall is much heavier. As early as September, these eastern passes may be blocked by snow; and they are not usually open again until the middle of June.

There is a section along the western shore of Honshu Island that faces the five-hundred-mile-wide Sea of Japan. Most of the surface of this sea remains ice-free all winter. As frigid winds sweep across from the Asiatic mainland, they pick up moisture from the warmer waters. Huge snowfalls occur when this cold, moisture-laden air reaches the lee shore of Honshu. In fact, records indicate that snow has fallen on more than one occasion for twenty-nine consecutive days. The depth of snow reported at this sea-level location is almost 150 inches. And it has remained in place for more than twenty weeks in a row.

Takata is located at approximately 37° N latitude in the Hokurika District of Honshu Island. A weather station has been maintained there since 1923. The station lies about sixty feet above sea level. It faces seaward and is backed by high mountains. The annual seasonal snowfall at this station is more than 262 inches. During the snowy season of 1944–45, a total of 362 inches fell. The heavy snowfall for that year came as no surprise because, by February 26, the snow cover on the ground already amounted to more than 148 inches. The ground was covered by snow from December 7, 1944, through April 25, 1945.

Freezing rain, freezing drizzle, and ice storms are also part of the winter scene. Freezing rain occurs when surface temperatures are below freezing, that is, below 32° F. The rain falls in liquid form, but freezes upon impact with the cold surface. This results in a coating of ice glaze on all exposed objects. The gen-

Wind lifts the fresh powder snow and sends it flying hither and yon.

eral term *ice storm* is used when freezing rain or drizzle occurs and produces a substantial glaze layer.

The ice that forms on exposed objects can range from a thin glaze to coatings more than one inch thick. Ice deposits to eight inches in diameter were reported on wires in northern Idaho in January, 1961. An evergreen tree standing to a height of fifty feet with an average width of approximately twenty feet may, under certain circumstances, be coated with as much as five tons of ice during a severe ice storm. Heavy accumulations of ice can wreck trees and transmission lines, especially when high winds accompany the storm.

The region in which ice storms hit most frequently is in a broad belt from Nebraska, Kansas, and Oklahoma eastward through the Middle Atlantic and New England States. But some of the most damaging struck during 1951 and blanketed the South with ice from January 28 through February 4. More than $50 million worth of damage was done in Mississippi alone. Louisiana and Arkansas also sustained millions of dollars' worth of damage.

A sleet storm is quite different from an ice storm. Sleet is frozen rain drops. The sleet falls as ice pellets. The ice pellets bounce when hitting the ground or other objects. The sleet does not stick to trees and wires.

Another common form of winter storm is a cold wave. During January, 1962, a brutal cold wave struck and held most of the country in its grip for more than a few weeks. Many low temperature records were broken. The 1962 cold wave was the result of a very deep trough in the *planetary wave* or jet stream. The trough, or depression, was centered over the Mississippi Valley. To the west of the trough, an extremely high ridge in the planetary wave acted like a funnel. Cold arctic air plummeted along the high ridge into the trough, and severe winter weather swept deep into the South.

The planetary wave is a meandering stream of winds some 30,000 feet above the surface. The way in which this jet stream meanders is a major factor in determining the earth's surface weather. As a result of the January, 1962, configuration in the planetary wave, cold air engulfed many areas of the South. El Paso, Texas, for example, plummeted to 8° below zero. Raleigh, North Carolina, recorded temperatures of 5° F, while thermometers in Virginia read 2° F. The temperatures in each of these locations were new all-time record low temperatures. An all-time low means that it is the lowest temperature recorded since record-keeping started around 1870.

At New Orleans, a 14° F reading was recorded on January 11, 1962. This set a new low for the month of January. Mobile, Alabama, recorded a temperature of 8°; Baton Rouge, Louisiana, 10°; Evansville, Indiana, 10° below zero; and Albuquerque, New Mexico, 6° below zero. These were all record lows for the month of January.

The United States Weather Bureau issues a cold-wave warning whenever it expects a rapid decline in the temperature within a twenty-four-hour period. A cold-wave warning means that precautionary measures should be taken to protect crops as well as industrial and commercial activities. Regardless of the month or the section of the country in which a cold-wave warn-

Crew members chop furiously to free the U. S. Coast Guard cutter Castlerock *of her 300-ton ice shroud caused by a severe winter storm in the Atlantic.*

ing is issued, the public should take careful note. A change to very cold weather always requires greater than normal protective measures to be taken.

Anyone who has been trapped outside knows that low temperatures and strong winds bring about a very rapid cooling of exposed surfaces. A very strong wind, combined with a temperature slightly below freezing, can produce a severe chilling effect. Face, hands, or any unprotected parts of the body seem to have the heat sucked out under these conditions. In fact, the chilling effect produced by this combination is approximately the same as you would experience if the temperature were nearly fifty degrees Fahrenheit lower in a calm atmosphere. A number, expressed as degrees, called the *wind-chill factor* is used to indicate what the combined effect of wind and temperature feels like. The wind-chill factor tells us the cooling effect of various wind and temperature combinations. The United States Weather Bureau usually issues this information as the *wind-chill index.*

A 10-mile-per-hour wind, for example, combined with a temperature of 20° F, affects you as though you were exposed to a temperature of 2° F. You would, in fact, feel very cold. If wind speed picks up and the temperature remains the same, you will feel much colder. The combination of a 20-mile-per-hour wind with the 20° F temperature gives a wind-chill index of 9° below zero. Rather than simply very cold, it will feel bitter cold to you even though the only real difference is the doubling of wind speed. In the event that the wind speed increases to 35 miles per hour while the temperature remains at 20° F, the wind-chill index would drop to minus 20° F. Under such conditions, you would feel *extremely* cold.

The Environmental Science Services Administration has developed a list of winter storm safety rules. These are good rules to study and to follow.

Keep ahead of the winter storm by listening to the latest ESSA Weather Bureau warnings and bulletins.

Check battery-powered equipment before the storm arrives. A portable radio or television set may be your only contact with the world outside the winter storm. Also check emergency cooking facilities and flashlights.

Check your supply of heating fuel. Fuel carriers may not be able to move if a winter storm buries your area in snow.

Check your food and stock an extra supply. Your supplies should include food that requires no cooking or refrigeration in case of power failure.

Prevent fire hazards due to overheated coal or oil burning stoves, fireplaces, heaters, or furnaces.

Stay indoors during storms and cold snaps unless in peak physical condition. If you must go out, avoid overexertion.

Don't kill yourself shoveling snow. It is extremely hard work for anyone in less than prime physical condition and can bring on a heart attack, a major cause of death during and after winter storms.

Rural residents: Make necessary trips for supplies before the storm develops or not at all; arrange for emergency heat supply in case of power failure; be sure camp stoves and lanterns are filled.

Dress to fit the season. If you spend much time outdoors, wear loose-fitting, lightweight, warm clothing in several layers; layers can be removed to prevent perspiring and subsequent chill. Outer garments should be tightly woven, water repellent, and hooded. The hood should protect much of your face and cover your mouth to ensure warm breathing and protect your lungs from the extremely cold air. Remember that entrapped, insulating air, warmed by body heat, is the best protection against cold. Layers of protective clothing are more effective and efficient than single layers of thick clothing; and mittens, snug at the wrists, are better protection than fingered gloves.

Your automobile can be your best friend—or worst enemy—during winter storms, depending on your preparations. Get your car winterized before the storm season begins. Everything on the checklist shown below should be taken care of before winter storms strike your area.

ignition system	*heater*
battery	*brakes perfectly adjusted*
lights	*wiper blades*
tire tread	*defroster*
cooling system	*snow tires installed*
fuel system	*chains*
lubrication	*antifreeze*
exhaust system tight	*winter-grade oil*

Keep water out of your fuel by maintaining a FULL tank of gasoline. Be equipped for the worst. Carry a winter storm car kit, especially if cross-country travel is anticipated or if you live in the northern states.

Suggested Winter Storm Car Kit: blankets or sleeping bags, matches and candles, empty 3-pound coffee can with plastic cover, facial tissue, paper towels, extra clothing, high-calorie, nonperishable food, compass and road maps, knife, first aid kit, shovel, sack of sand, flashlight or signal light, windshield scraper, booster cables, two tow chains, fire extinguisher, catalytic heater, ax. Winter travel by automobile is serious business. Take your travel seriously:

If the storm exceeds or even tests your limitations, seek available refuge immediately.

Plan your travel and select primary and alternate routes. Check latest weather information on your radio.

Try not to travel alone; two or three persons are preferable. Travel in convoy with another vehicle, if possible.

Always fill gasoline tank before entering open country, even a short distance.

Drive carefully, defensively.

11. Killer
from the Sea

The roughest coastal waters in the United States are around Yaquina Bay, Oregon. A fifty-two-foot motor lifeboat charges through a rough breaker. These breakers, however, are puny and insignificant compared to the tsunamis produced by earthquakes.

11. Killer from the Sea

The Prince William Sound earthquake of March 27, 1964, was one of the largest shocks ever recorded on the North American continent. Its epicenter was located at approximately 61 ° N latitude and 148 ° W longitude, which placed it somewhere between Crescent Glacier and Unakwik Inlet. The magnitude of the shock on the Richter scale was almost 8.5.

This earthquake generated ocean waves of record size that destroyed much of Valdez, Alaska. Thirty-one people in that city lost their lives. In addition, the waves struck south and produced extensive destruction and loss of life in Crescent City, California. At Crescent City, eleven people lost their lives and an estimated $7.5 million worth of damage was done. The sea waves continued to roll south, passed southern California and Mexico, and then went on to the shores of Chile. The waves from the Alaskan earthquake also moved across the Pacific, touching Hawaii and Japan.

Ocean waves generated by an earthquake are called *seismic sea waves,* or *tsunamis.* In other words, a tsunami is the destructive oceanic offspring of an earthquake or seism. The name "tsunami," used internationally, comes from the Japanese, whose islands have felt the destructive power of these terrible killers from the sea for generations.

The settlers on the islands and continental rims of the Pacific Ocean live in constant fear of the tsunami. These great waves have come again and again, bringing devastation and death with them. The Krakatoa catastrophe of 1883 took the lives of about thirty-six thousand persons. These deaths were not due to the explosion of the volcano, but were, in fact, due to the succession of enormous sea waves generated by the explosion. The Krakatoa tsunamis reached one hundred feet in height and swept away many of the villages on the low-lying coasts of Java and Sumatra.

Krakatoa is a volcanic isle situated in the Sunda Strait between Java and Sumatra. The volcano is, in fact, one of more than one hundred active and recently-active volcanoes that dot the Indonesian islands. The area in which these volcanoes are found represents the greatest concentration of volcanic activity in the world.

The eruptions that produced Krakatoa have been going on for centuries. An eruption in 1680, for example, plunged the crater below sea level. Then the volcanoes in this group lay dormant for two hundred years. In 1880, a series of earthquakes indicated Krakatoa and its neighbors had awakened from their long sleep. Along with the quakes, tsunamis rolled out across the sea. Shocks rocked the area for three years and during that time sea waves of various heights rolled throughout the area.

In May, 1883, tremendous clouds of steam and ash soared out of Krakatoa to heights of seven miles. Finally, on August 27, at 10 A.M., two enormous explosions shook earth and sky; and two

This is a scene from the motion picture Krakatoa, East of Java.

of the three cones making up Krakatoa were blown to bits. The extreme violence of the explosion resulted from the sudden inrush of large volumes of sea water into side fissures. The inrushing sea water produced an enormous amount of superheated steam. The steam, expanding in all directions, literally tore the island apart.

The explosion of Krakatoa discharged nearly five cubic miles of rock fragments into the air. Tremendous quantities of ash fell over an area of more than 300,000 square miles. In the Sunda Strait itself, the ash in the air blocked the sun and produced total darkness. Ships reaching the Sunda Strait just after the waves had struck reported that the waters were clogged with pumice. In addition to the pumice and darkness, the strait was filled with the dead bodies of men, women, and children. The fine dust from Krakatoa rose high into the stratosphere. Throughout the following year, it drifted several times around the earth and gave rise to spectacular red sunsets all over the world.

On the morning of August 28, the volcano was quiet again. Small explosions, however, did occur on September 17, 26, and October 10, 1883. Then, after a silence of some four months, another small explosion occurred on February 28, 1884, but by this time the great convulsions were over.

The tsunamis generated by Krakatoa's explosion of 1883 were recorded on the tide gauges throughout the world. The waves reached out across the Pacific and struck Hawaii. The Krakatoa tsunamis were also recorded in South America. The greatest of these waves was generated just after the explosion of 10 A.M. on August 27. It built to a height of 120 feet.

On December 29, 1927, new eruptions started on the sea floor in the vicinity of Krakatoa. The intensity of the shocks grew as huge jets of cinder and ash broke through the surface of the sea. On January 26, 1928, a volcanic cone with its base on the ocean floor poked its head above the surface of the sea to establish a small island. The island was named Anak Krakatoa, which means "child of Krakatoa." Volcanic activity of Anak Krakatoa continued and, by 1953, it had built itself to a height of 360 feet above sea level. During the 1960s, it was still active. With each eruption of Anak Krakatoa and any of the other volcanoes in the area, there is the possibility that tsunamis will form, move out, and carry destruction far and wide across the Pacific.

Around the Pacific Ocean there is a zone of tremendous seismic activity. This circumpacific seismic belt moves along major geologic faults, or fractures, in the earth. In South America, it moves from the south of Chile up the Pacific coast of South America into the coastal region of Central America and then on up the Pacific coast of the United States. It turns westward along the Aleutian Islands arc and then southward toward Japan and the Philippine Republic. From this point, the seismic belt branches westward to Malaysia and Indonesia. Turning eastward, it moves through New Guinea, the southern island groups, and New Zealand.

The seismic belt ringing the Pacific Ocean produces some of the greatest convulsions in the earth's crust and, as a result, is the spawning ground for tsunamis. Some of these devastating waves are believed to be caused by vertical fault movements.

On November 14, 1963, eruptions broke the surface of the Atlantic Ocean near Iceland and a new volcanic island called Surtsey was born. Whenever volcanic eruptions and earthquakes occur in the ocean or close to it, there is a danger that tsunamis will spring from the disturbance.

Others may have their origin as a result of submarine landslides initiated by earthquakes.

In the open ocean, the height of a tsunami or its wave amplitude is very small. At most, a tsunami will not be more than two or three feet high in an open sea. Thus, they cause no problem at all to ships in mid-ocean or well beyond the reach of the shoreline.

The wave length of a tsunami, or the distance from crest to crest, may be more than one hundred miles. Again, if we relate this information to an observation you might make from a ship at sea, we must say that you would not recognize that a tsunami passed. In other words, a wave with a height, or amplitude, of two or three feet would roll by; then, fifteen or thirty minutes later, another wave of approximately the same height would follow.

The elapsed time, that is, the time it takes two successive crests to pass a fixed location, is called the *wave period*. The time from crest to crest, or the wave period, for tsunamis ranges from fifteen to thirty minutes.

The waves of a tsunami do not travel at a uniform speed. The speed at which they move depends upon the depth of the water. A tsunami travels at speeds ranging from about 150 miles per hour in water that is 1,600 feet deep to about 670 miles per hour in water 30,000 feet deep.

While it is true that the amplitude of a tsunami is small in the open ocean, the amplitude, or height, from crest to trough changes dramatically as the shore is approached. As the tsunami enters the shoaling water of a coastline, the wave velocity diminishes while its wave height increases. This change in velocity and height occurs as the tsunami encounters shallow water. The bottom of the ocean interferes with the movement of any waves and the tsunami obeys the general laws of wave physics as it "feels" bottom.

At a water depth equal to one-half its wave length, the solid bottom of the sea changes the tsunami's velocity. Frictional drag against the sea floor causes a loss of wave energy and, thus, a decrease in tsunami velocity. A tsunami, for example, moves at a speed of 670 miles per hour when the water depth is 30,000 feet; but when the depth decreases to 24,000 feet, the velocity of the wave drops to 600 miles per hour. In water depths of 18,000 feet, the tsunami travels at speeds of 519 miles an hour. Velocity is cut to 424 miles an hour when it moves across water depths of 12,000 feet. When it encounters bottoms at 6,000 feet, the tsunami slows to 299 miles per hour. In depths of 3,000 feet, its speed is 212 miles per hour, while it moves along at no more than 94 miles per hour through water with a depth of 600 feet. The tsunami speed is slashed to a mere 30 miles per hour in water depths of 60 feet.

Two additional conditions develop as a result of the tsunami's "feeling" bottom and having its velocity altered. The first very obvious fact is that, as the velocity of the wave decreases, its length will be affected. The wave length of the tsunami decreases because the following crest begins to draw closer to the crest in front which is slowing as it "feels" bottom. Then, as a result of the decrease in velocity and wave length, the wave begins to steepen dramatically. The crest builds to fantastic heights.

The arrival of a tsunami begins with what appears as an abnormally low tide. The coastal waters actually recede because a trough moves in advance of the crest of the initial wave. The low tide develops in a matter of minutes and exposes the ocean floor far beyond the limits of normal low tides. The abnormal lowering of the water level heralds that the steepening tsunami wave is not far behind. The wave which in the open ocean had an amplitude of a mere three feet, steepens with each decrease in its velocity until it develops amplitudes of more than 100 feet. These tremendous waves strike with devastating force.

The tsunami generated by the Aleutian earthquake of April 1, 1946, moved across the Pacific toward the Hawaiian Islands. When it arrived, its waves steepened to heights of 55 feet. More than 150 lives were lost and five hundred homes were demolished by the wave as it moved inland. The waves that moved south from the 1946 Aleutian disturbance toward the California coast struck Santa Cruz with amplitudes of more than 12 feet.

In the Prince William Sound earthquake of March, 1964, the major tsunami was generated by broad, crustal warping along a northeast-southwest line. The motion of the water was extremely complex within the generating area. In fact, other waves, in addition to the major tsunami, were generated by local tides. Then, to add to the muddle, refraction, defraction, and reflection of the wave patterns occurred within Prince William Sound. All of this contributed to the complexity of the seismic waves that moved out of the area.

Local waves generated in many of the harbors and bays as a result of the landslides that occurred below the sea surface proved to be very destructive. The most devastating local waves struck at Seward, Valdez, and Whittier. At Seward, for example, a stretch of the waterfront about 3,500 feet long and 300 feet wide, including all the pier facilities, slid into Resurrection Bay. This slide occurred shortly after the earthquake started and while the shaking was still intense. The slide itself drew water away from the shoreline and created two of its own disturbances at distances of one-half mile from the shore. Waves spread in all directions as a result of the landslide. The initial shock of the earthquake had ruptured waterfront fuel storage tanks. The oil from these tanks ignited immediately. The waves generated by the landslide spread the fiery oil throughout the area.

Seismic seiches are oscillations (waves) generated in closed or partially-closed bodies of water by the surface waves of earthquakes. Earthquakes with significant magnitudes may produce seiches at tremendous distances from the source. The great Lisbon, Portugal, earthquake of 1755, for example, set up seiches all over western Europe. Loch Lomond, a lake in Scotland, oscillated for an hour. The waves produced in the lake developed an amplitude of about two feet.

The Prince William Sound earthquake of 1964 generated seiche action in bodies of water as far away as the Gulf of Mexico. Oscillations were observed in rivers, harbors, channels, lakes, and even swimming pools throughout the continental United States. Seiche damage, although generally minor, was widespread along a good portion of the Gulf coast. The area in which damage occurred extended from Lake Borgne, Louisiana, in the east to Houston, Texas, in the west. Seiche action from the Gulf was reported as far inland as Baton Rouge, Louisiana. Damage reported near Golden Meadow and Galliano, Louisiana, included flooding along both sides of Bayou Lafourche. A number of boats in the same vicinity sank or were washed ashore. A large oyster vessel broke loose from its moorings and heaved into a dockside store.

All ocean waves, including tsunamis, conform to simple physical laws.

The 8th Naval District Headquarters at New Orleans reported a sudden rise of one and one-half feet in the Mississippi River. This seiche action caused vessels at the wharf to lurch and mooring lines to break. An eighty-three-foot United States Coast Guard cutter and a barge parted their mooring lines in the Industrial Canal. In the Harvey Canal across the Mississippi from New Orleans, a number of barges were set adrift from a surge that had an amplitude of about two and one-half feet.

The velocity of a tsunami wave varies with water depth. It is this relationship that permits observers to predict a tsunami's arrival time at all points in the Pacific Ocean area. Eight minutes after the beginning of the Prince William Sound earthquake, for example, the seismic waves it generated reached Hawaii. These seismic, or earthquake, waves, moving through the solid earth, triggered the alarm attached to the seismograph located at the United States Coast and Geodetic Survey's Honolulu Observatory. The scientists at the observatory went into action immediately. The photographic record of the seismogram was examined immediately, and the Hawaiian civil defense authorities were notified of the earthquake. The observatory in Honolulu sent requests for seismic readings to various observatories throughout the world. The first seismic report received from another observatory was from Manila. It gave the P reading for the Manila Observatory. In a short time, enough information had been received to permit the Honolulu Observatory to locate the earthquake epicenter near Seward, Alaska. The Honolulu Observatory immediately computed the estimated arrival time of the tsunami for various locations in the Pacific.

The city of Kodiak, Alaska, was fortunate indeed. The residents of the city had a thirty-minute warning before the first crest of the tsunami struck. The first wave produced a tidal flood followed by a gradual ebb. The second wave of the tsunami advanced as a cresting thirty-foot wall of water that thundered through the channel and pushed 50- to 150-ton boats over the

This scene shows tsunami damage produced by the Alaskan earthquake of 1964. A heavy buoy in the foreground was ripped free from its moorings and thrown ashore. Note the size of the ship that was also cast ashore by the seismic wave. A large dump truck stands before the ship on the right. Note the relative size of the dump truck to the ship.

breakwater. Some of these huge boats were thrown more than three blocks into the city.

The Canadian government, in July, 1963, withdrew from the Seismic Sea Wave Warning System that began functioning in 1948. Thus, no official warning of the tsunami was provided to Canada since it was out of the system for almost a year. Unfortunately, the tsunami from the Alaskan earthquake of 1964 struck the Canadian coast near the time of high tide. The tsunami wave, coupled with the water levels of high tide, produced extensive destruction. The twin cities of Alberni and Port Alberni sustained the most damage. The highest wave reported in Canada was at Shields Bay on the west coast of Graham Island. The crest was almost thirty-two feet high and the waves severely damaged a logging camp.

The tragedy in Canada was compounded by the lack of Canadian interest in being a part of the international seismic sea warning system. The twin cities of Alberni and Port Alberni are about thirty-five miles from the open ocean at the head of the long, narrow Alberni Inlet. The tsunami moved up this narrow passageway and swept into the towns. The effect of the first wave was devastating. The worst flooding conditions in the area had never caused anything like the damage of the tsunami. The second crest of almost twenty-one feet was the highest. But, fortunately, because of the shape of the inlet, the period from the first to the second crest was ninety-seven minutes. Thus, after the initial wave hit, the inhabitants of these cities were alert to the danger that would most certainly follow. In the hour and one-half before the second crest arrived, many of them left the low-lying areas and got to safer positions on higher ground.

The Pacific Tsunami Warning System is operated by ESSA's Coast and Geodetic Survey. Its headquarters is located near Honolulu. The system monitors seismological and tidal installations in Hawaii and other locations around the Pacific Ocean. A tsunami watch is issued by ESSA whenever an earthquake with sufficient magnitude to generate a tsunami occurs. The scientists at the warning center determine the location of the earthquake epicenter. If the epicenter is under or near the ocean, they know that tsunami generation is possible. On the basis of the seismic evidence available to them, the scientists at the center send out a bulletin which indicates that an earthquake has occurred. They broadcast the location of the epicenter and indicate that the possibility of a tsunami exists.

The first positive indication that a tsunami has been generated usually comes from tide stations nearest the disturbance. As soon as they are able to confirm that a tsunami exists, the scientists at the center issue a tsunami warning. They immediately distribute the estimated time of arrival of the tsunami at all locations.

The great seismic sea waves cannot be stopped. But the damage they produce can be minimized and people can live through the disaster by following these safety rules:

Not all earthquakes cause tsunamis, but many do. When you hear that an earthquake has occurred, stand by for a tsunami emergency.

An earthquake in your area is a natural tsunami warning. Do not stay in low-lying coastal areas after a local earthquake.

A tsunami is not a single wave, but a series of waves. Stay out of danger areas until an "all-clear" is issued by competent authority.

Approaching tsunamis are sometimes heralded by a noticeable rise or fall of coastal water. This is nature's tsunami warning, and it should be heeded.

A small tsunami at one beach can be a giant a few miles away. Don't let the modest size of one make you lose respect for all.

The National Tsunami Warning Center does not issue false alarms. When a warning is issued, a tsunami exists. The tsunami of May 1960 killed 61 in Hilo, Hawaii, who thought it was "just another false alarm."

All tsunamis—like hurricanes—are potentially dangerous, even though they may not damage every coastline they strike.

Never go down to the beach to watch for a tsunami. When you can see the wave, you are too close to escape it.

Sooner or later, tsunamis visit every coastline in the Pacific. Warnings apply to you if you live in any Pacific coastal area.

During a tsunami emergency, your local Civil Defense, police, and other emergency organizations will try to save your life. Give them your fullest cooperation.

JOHN GABRIEL NAVARRA, the author of *Nature Strikes Back*, is Professor of Geoscience and was, for ten years, Chairman of the Division of Science at Jersey City State College. As both a teacher and a writer, Dr. Navarra has an international reputation. He was the teacher of the first televised science course to be offered in the South when he was on the faculty of East Carolina University. He has written a number of trade books for young readers, adult science books, and is the senior author of a complete series of science textbooks, grades kindergarten through nine, that are used by millions of school children throughout the United States. Dr. Navarra traveled extensively to do research on his new book.

Index

Index